**PRENTICE HALL MATHEMATICS**

# ALGEBRA 2

# Chapter 4
# Support File

## Matrices

Prentice
Hall

Needham, Massachusetts
Upper Saddle River, New Jersey
Glenview, Illinois

ISBN: 0-13-063822-6

1 2 3 4 5 6 7 8 9 10   06 05 04 03 02

# Chapter 4

## *Matrices*

# Practice 4-1

**Organizing Data into Matrices**

Write the dimensions of each matrix. Identify the indicated element.

**1.** $\begin{bmatrix} 2 \\ -3 \\ -6 \end{bmatrix}; a_{21}$

**2.** $\begin{bmatrix} 5 & -7 & 23 & 10 \\ -9 & 3 & 5 & -2 \\ 1 & 9 & 0 & 2 \end{bmatrix}; a_{23}$

**3.** $\begin{bmatrix} 2 & 3 & -9 \\ 12 & -8 & 0 \end{bmatrix}; a_{21}$

**4.** $\begin{bmatrix} x & y & z \\ a & b & c \\ p & q & r \end{bmatrix}; a_{32}$

**5.** $\begin{bmatrix} 2 & -2 \\ 3 & -3 \\ 4 & -4 \end{bmatrix}; a_{31}$

**6.** $[5 \quad 8 \quad -7 \quad -4]; a_{14}$

**Use the table for Exercises 7–10.**

**7.** Display the data in a matrix with the types of unemployment in the columns.

**8.** State the dimensions of the matrix.

**9.** Identify $a_{21}$, and tell what it represents.

**10.** Identify $a_{16}$, and tell what it represents.

**Unemployment by Category**

|  | June, 1992 | June, 1996 |
|---|---|---|
| **Construction** | 17.6% | 9.5% |
| **Manufacturing** | 8.3% | 5.1% |
| **Transportation** | 5.4% | 4.5% |
| **Sales** | 8.7% | 6.4% |
| **Finance** | 4.0% | 2.6% |
| **Services** | 6.6% | 5.1% |
| **Government** | 3.5% | 2.7% |

Source: *U.S. News & World Report*

**Use the table at the right for Exercises 11–14.**

**11.** Write a matrix $M$ to represent the data in the graph, with columns representing years.

**12.** What are the dimensions of this matrix?

**13.** What does the first row represent?

**14.** What does $m_{32}$ represent?

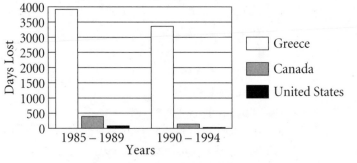

**Days Lost to Strikes per 1,000 Employees**

Source: *U.S. News & World Report*

# Practice 4-2

**Adding and Subtracting Matrices**

**Find the value of each variable.**

**1.** $\begin{bmatrix} a & 2b \\ c-2 & d+3 \end{bmatrix} = \begin{bmatrix} 5 & -7 \\ 10 & 10 \end{bmatrix}$

**2.** $\begin{bmatrix} 3 & 5 & -y & x \\ z & 0 & 3a & b \end{bmatrix} = \begin{bmatrix} 3 & 3c & 7 & 4 \\ \frac{7}{2} & 0 & -9 & 3b \end{bmatrix}$

**3.** $\begin{bmatrix} 5 & 1 \\ 0 & 2 \end{bmatrix} + \begin{bmatrix} 2 & -13 \\ -10 & -10 \end{bmatrix} = \begin{bmatrix} 2x+1 & -4x \\ 5z & 2.5z-x \end{bmatrix}$

**Use the information in the table.**

**4.** Put the data in two matrices: one for males and one for females.

**5.** Use matrix subtraction to find the difference between the number of males and the number of females in each club each year.

**Club Membership at TC High School**

| | 1961–1962 | | 2001–2002 | |
|---|---|---|---|---|
| | **Males** | **Females** | **Males** | **Females** |
| **Beta** | 37 | 23 | 56 | 58 |
| **Spanish** | 0 | 93 | 76 | 82 |
| **Chess** | 87 | 0 | 102 | 34 |
| **Library** | 6 | 18 | 27 | 29 |

**Find each sum or difference.**

**6.** $\begin{bmatrix} -1 & 2 \\ 3 & -1 \end{bmatrix} + \begin{bmatrix} -1 & 2 \\ -3 & 1 \end{bmatrix} + \begin{bmatrix} 0 & -1 \\ 2 & 0 \end{bmatrix}$

**7.** $\begin{bmatrix} 8 & -5 & -5 \\ 4 & -10 & 10 \\ 2 & -15 & -15 \end{bmatrix} - \begin{bmatrix} 0 & 0 & 1 \\ 1 & -2 & -2 \\ -2 & -3 & 3 \end{bmatrix}$

**8.** $\begin{bmatrix} -2 & -1 \\ -3 & 1 \\ -1 & -1 \end{bmatrix} - \begin{bmatrix} -2 & -2 \\ 3 & -1 \\ 0 & -2 \end{bmatrix} + \begin{bmatrix} -2 & 1 \\ 0 & 3 \\ -3 & -3 \end{bmatrix}$

**9.** $\begin{bmatrix} 1 \\ 1 \\ 1 \end{bmatrix} + \begin{bmatrix} -1 \\ -3 \\ 5 \end{bmatrix} + \begin{bmatrix} -10 \\ -7 \\ 11 \end{bmatrix} - \begin{bmatrix} -3 \\ -5 \\ -6 \end{bmatrix}$

**Solve each matrix equation.**

**10.** $X - \begin{bmatrix} 3 & 4 \\ 4 & 2 \\ 1 & 9 \end{bmatrix} = \begin{bmatrix} 5 & 7 \\ 9 & 12 \\ 3 & 2 \end{bmatrix}$

**11.** $X + \begin{bmatrix} 20 & -9 & -3 \\ 19 & -2 & -5 \\ -1 & 0 & -8 \end{bmatrix} = \begin{bmatrix} -7 & 92 & -5 \\ 0 & 91 & -6 \\ -9 & -1 & 12 \end{bmatrix}$

**12.** $\begin{bmatrix} -2 & -3 \\ 2 & 2 \end{bmatrix} = X - \begin{bmatrix} 1 & -1 \\ -2 & 2 \end{bmatrix}$

**13.** $\begin{bmatrix} 2 & 2 & 0 \\ 1 & -1 & -1 \end{bmatrix} = \begin{bmatrix} 2 & -2 & 3 \\ -3 & -3 & 4 \end{bmatrix} - X$

**Determine whether the two matrices in each pair are equal. Justify your reasoning.**

**14.** $\begin{bmatrix} 2 \\ \sqrt{9} \\ 16 \end{bmatrix} ; \begin{bmatrix} \frac{4}{2} & 3 & 4^2 \end{bmatrix}$

**15.** $\begin{bmatrix} 2(3) & 3(1.5) \\ 7 & \frac{10}{2} \end{bmatrix} ; \begin{bmatrix} 6 & 4.5 \\ 7 & 5 \end{bmatrix}$

# Practice 4-3

Use matrices *A*, *B*, *C*, *D*, and *E* to find each product, sum, or difference, if possible. If not possible, write *product undefined*, *sum undefined*, or *difference undefined*.

$$A = \begin{bmatrix} 1 & -1 \\ 3 & -2 \end{bmatrix} \qquad B = \begin{bmatrix} 0 & 2 \\ -2 & 1 \\ -1 & 0 \end{bmatrix} \qquad C = \begin{bmatrix} 3 & -3 & -1 \\ 2 & -2 & 4 \end{bmatrix} \qquad D = \begin{bmatrix} 1 & 0 \\ 0 & 1 \end{bmatrix} \qquad E = \begin{bmatrix} 3 \\ -3 \\ 2 \end{bmatrix}$$

**1.** $3AB$

**2.** $2A + 4D$

**3.** $5D - A$

**4.** $2C - E$

**5.** $3D + A$

**6.** $DA$

**7.** $AE$

**8.** $BD$

**9.** $DB$

**10.** $CE$

**11.** $DC$

**12.** $EB$

**13.** $CB$

**14.** $2D$

**15.** $BE$

**16.** $0.2B$

**17.** $\frac{1}{4}C$

**18.** $0.5AC$

**19.** $DE$

**20.** $-3DE$

Find the dimensions of the product matrix. Then find each product.

**21.** $\begin{bmatrix} 1 \\ 2 \\ 3 \end{bmatrix} \begin{bmatrix} 1 & 2 & 3 & 4 \end{bmatrix}$

**22.** $\begin{bmatrix} 1 & 2 & 12 \\ 12 & 2 & 1 \end{bmatrix} \begin{bmatrix} 3 & 4 \\ 4 & 3 \\ 5 & 2 \end{bmatrix}$

**23.** $\begin{bmatrix} 1 & 2 \\ 2 & 1 \end{bmatrix} \begin{bmatrix} 2 & 1 \\ 1 & 2 \end{bmatrix}$

Find each product if possible. If not possible, write *product undefined*.

**24.** $-12 \begin{bmatrix} -6 & -2 \\ -5 & -6 \\ 0 & 1 \end{bmatrix}$

**25.** $\begin{bmatrix} 3 & 2 \\ 4 & 6 \\ 1 & 1 \end{bmatrix} \begin{bmatrix} -3 & 3 & -2 \\ -2 & 5 & -1 \end{bmatrix}$

**26.** $\begin{bmatrix} 0 & 1 & 0 \\ 2 & 2 & 1 \end{bmatrix} \begin{bmatrix} -2 & 2 & 2 \\ -1 & 1 & 1 \\ 0 & -1 & -1 \end{bmatrix}$

**27.** $\begin{bmatrix} 1 & 1 & 1 \\ 1 & 1 & 1 \\ 1 & 1 & 1 \end{bmatrix} \begin{bmatrix} 2 & 3 \\ 4 & 1 \\ 5 & 6 \end{bmatrix}$

**28.** $\begin{bmatrix} 1 & 0 & 1 \\ 1 & 1 & 0 \\ 1 & 1 & 1 \end{bmatrix} \begin{bmatrix} 6 & 4 & 2 & 8 \\ 10 & 4 & 6 & 2 \\ 2 & 10 & 12 & 4 \end{bmatrix}$

**29.** $\begin{bmatrix} 4 & 3 \\ 9 & 7 \end{bmatrix} \begin{bmatrix} 6 & 3 \\ 9 & 4 \end{bmatrix}$

Solve each equation. Check your answers.

**30.** $2 \begin{bmatrix} 0 & 1 \\ 3 & -4 \end{bmatrix} - 3X = \begin{bmatrix} 9 & -6 \\ 1 & -2 \end{bmatrix}$

**31.** $\frac{1}{2}X + \begin{bmatrix} 5 & -1 \\ 0 & \frac{2}{3} \end{bmatrix} = 2 \begin{bmatrix} 3 & 0 \\ 1 & 2 \end{bmatrix}$

# Practice 4-4

**Geometric Transformations with Matrices**

For Exercises 1–11, use $\triangle ABC$ at the right. Find the coordinates of the image under each transformation. Express your answer as a matrix.

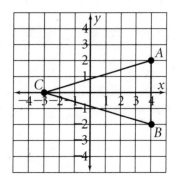

1. a dilation of 11

2. a translation 1 unit right and 4 units up

3. a dilation of 1.5

4. a translation 2 units right and 6 units down

5. a reflection in $y = x$

6. a rotation of 270°

7. a rotation of 90°

8. a translation 1 unit left and 2 units down

9. a translation 3 units left and 1 unit up

10. a dilation of $\frac{1}{2}$

11. a reflection in the $x$-axis

**Graph each figure and its image after the given transformation.**

12. $\begin{bmatrix} 2 & -3 & 6 & 4 \\ 0 & 1 & 1 & -4 \end{bmatrix}$; a dilation of 2

13. $\begin{bmatrix} 8 & 3 & -2 & -5 & 2 \\ 7 & 6 & 1 & 0 & -4 \end{bmatrix}$; a translation 2 units left and 1 unit up

14. $\begin{bmatrix} 2 & 4 & 5 & 3 \\ 1 & 1 & 3 & 5 \end{bmatrix}$; a translation 5 units left and 4 units down

15. $\begin{bmatrix} 2 & 1 & 6 & -4 \\ 0 & -3 & 5 & -2 \end{bmatrix}$; a rotation of 180°

16. $\begin{bmatrix} 6 & 5 & 1 & -3 & 6 \\ -1 & 6 & 2 & 0 & -4 \end{bmatrix}$; a reflection in the $y$-axis

**The coordinates of the vertices of a polygon are given. Represent each transformation with matrices. Then express the coordinates of the vertices of the image as a matrix.**

17. $I(21, -14), J(0, -7), K(-14, 0), L(0, 7)$; a dilation of $\frac{1}{7}$

18. $M(2, 0), N(0, -2), P(-2, 0)$; a translation 2 units down

19. $Q(2, 0), R(0, -2), S(-2, 0)$; a reflection in $y = -x$

# Practice 4-5

**2 × 2 Matrices, Determinants, and Inverses**

Find the matrix $E^{-1}$ for each.

**1.** $E = \begin{bmatrix} 2 & -2 \\ -1 & 2 \end{bmatrix}$

**2.** $E = \begin{bmatrix} 1 & -1 \\ 1 & 1 \end{bmatrix}$

**3.** $E = \begin{bmatrix} 2 & -1 \\ 1 & 0 \end{bmatrix}$

**4.** $E = \begin{bmatrix} 2 & 3 \\ 1 & 1 \end{bmatrix}$

**5.** $E = \begin{bmatrix} 1 & 4 \\ 1 & 3 \end{bmatrix}$

**6.** $E = \begin{bmatrix} 4 & 7 \\ 3 & 5 \end{bmatrix}$

Find the inverse of each matrix, if it exists. If it does not exist, write
*no inverse* and explain why not.

**7.** $\begin{bmatrix} 3 & 4 \\ -3 & 4 \end{bmatrix}$

**8.** $\begin{bmatrix} 3 & 4 \\ 3 & 4 \end{bmatrix}$

**9.** $\begin{bmatrix} 1 & 2 \\ 3 & 4 \end{bmatrix}$

**10.** $\begin{bmatrix} 30 & -4 \\ -25 & 3 \end{bmatrix}$

Solve each matrix equation.

**11.** $\begin{bmatrix} 1 & 2 \\ -1 & -2 \end{bmatrix} X = \begin{bmatrix} 2 \\ -2 \end{bmatrix}$

**12.** $\begin{bmatrix} 1 & 1 \\ 1 & -1 \end{bmatrix} X = \begin{bmatrix} 3 \\ -1 \end{bmatrix}$

**13.** $\begin{bmatrix} -2 & 3 \\ -4 & 5 \end{bmatrix} X = \begin{bmatrix} 6 \\ 8 \end{bmatrix}$

Evaluate the determinant of each matrix.

**14.** $\begin{bmatrix} -3 & 4 \\ 1 & -1 \end{bmatrix}$

**15.** $\begin{bmatrix} 3 & 9 \\ 3 & 2 \end{bmatrix}$

**16.** $\begin{bmatrix} 1 & -4 \\ 2 & 6 \end{bmatrix}$

**17.** $\begin{bmatrix} 4 & -3 \\ 1 & -8 \end{bmatrix}$

**18.** $\begin{bmatrix} 5 & 4 \\ 4 & 5 \end{bmatrix}$

**19.** $\begin{bmatrix} 1 & -12 \\ 3 & 0 \end{bmatrix}$

Determine whether the matrices are multiplicative inverses.

**20.** $\begin{bmatrix} 2 & 1 \\ 5 & 3 \end{bmatrix}, \begin{bmatrix} 3 & -1 \\ -5 & 2 \end{bmatrix}$

**21.** $\begin{bmatrix} 4 & 9 \\ 2 & 6 \end{bmatrix}, \begin{bmatrix} 1 & -\frac{3}{2} \\ -\frac{1}{3} & \frac{2}{3} \end{bmatrix}$

**22.** $\begin{bmatrix} 1 & 2 \\ 3 & 4 \end{bmatrix}, \begin{bmatrix} -2 & 1 \\ \frac{3}{2} & -\frac{1}{2} \end{bmatrix}$

# Practice 4-6

**Where necessary, use a graphing calculator. Find the inverse ($A^{-1}$) of each matrix, if it exists. If it does not exist, write *no inverse*.**

**1.** $\begin{bmatrix} 1 & 2 & 0 \\ -2 & 0 & -3 \\ 3 & -1 & 5 \end{bmatrix}$
**2.** $\begin{bmatrix} 1 & 1 & 1 \\ 2 & 1 & 0 \\ 0 & 2 & 3 \end{bmatrix}$
**3.** $\begin{bmatrix} 2 & 4 & 3 \\ 0 & 5 & -1 \\ 1 & -1 & 2 \end{bmatrix}$
**4.** $\begin{bmatrix} 0 & 2 & 0 \\ 2 & 0 & 2 \\ 0 & 2 & 0 \end{bmatrix}$

**5.** $\begin{bmatrix} 4 & 5 & 6 \\ 0 & 1 & 2 \\ 8 & 9 & 5 \end{bmatrix}$
**6.** $\begin{bmatrix} 1 & -1 & 1 \\ 0 & 0 & 0 \\ 0 & 0 & 1 \end{bmatrix}$
**7.** $\begin{bmatrix} -1 & 0 & -1 \\ 0 & -2 & 0 \\ -2 & 0 & 3 \end{bmatrix}$
**8.** $\begin{bmatrix} -3 & -2 & -1 \\ 0 & 1 & 2 \\ 3 & 4 & -4 \end{bmatrix}$

**Solve each equation for $X$.**

**9.** $\begin{bmatrix} 1 & 0 & 0 \\ 0 & 1 & 0 \\ 0 & 0 & 1 \end{bmatrix} X = \begin{bmatrix} 4 \\ -5 \\ 3 \end{bmatrix}$
**10.** $\begin{bmatrix} 1 & 2 & 0 \\ -2 & 0 & -3 \\ 3 & -1 & 5 \end{bmatrix} X = \begin{bmatrix} -1 \\ 12 \\ -20 \end{bmatrix}$
**11.** $\begin{bmatrix} 0 & 0 & 1 \\ 0 & 0 & 1 \\ 1 & 1 & 1 \end{bmatrix} X = \begin{bmatrix} 3 \\ 4 \\ 3 \end{bmatrix}$

**Evaluate the determinant of each matrix.**

**12.** $\begin{bmatrix} -1 & 2 & -2 \\ 0 & 1 & 3 \\ 4 & 2 & -1 \end{bmatrix}$
**13.** $\begin{bmatrix} 2 & 1 & 2 \\ -1 & 0 & 5 \\ 0 & 4 & 1 \end{bmatrix}$
**14.** $\begin{bmatrix} 2 & 4 & 3 \\ -3 & 0 & -2 \\ -1 & 3 & 0 \end{bmatrix}$

**15.** $\begin{bmatrix} 2 & 6 & -1 \\ 1 & 0 & 0 \\ 1 & 3 & -2 \end{bmatrix}$
**16.** $\begin{bmatrix} -4 & 0 & 3 \\ 0 & -2 & 3 \\ -1 & 4 & -2 \end{bmatrix}$
**17.** $\begin{bmatrix} 7 & -1 & 3 \\ 1 & 2 & 6 \\ 4 & 1 & 3 \end{bmatrix}$

**Determine whether the matrices are multiplicative inverses.**

**18.** $A = \begin{bmatrix} -2 & 2 & 3 \\ 1 & -1 & 0 \\ 0 & 1 & 4 \end{bmatrix}, B = \begin{bmatrix} -\frac{4}{3} & -\frac{5}{3} & 1 \\ -\frac{4}{3} & -\frac{8}{3} & 1 \\ 1 & \frac{2}{3} & 0 \end{bmatrix}$
**19.** $A = \begin{bmatrix} 2 & -17 & 11 \\ -1 & 11 & -7 \\ 0 & 3 & -2 \end{bmatrix}, B = \begin{bmatrix} 1 & 1 & 2 \\ 2 & 4 & -3 \\ 3 & 6 & -5 \end{bmatrix}$

# Practice 4-7

**Solve each system.**

**1.** $\begin{cases} x + y + z = 0.621 \\ 3x - 3y + 2z = -0.007 \\ 4x + 5y - 10z = 1.804 \end{cases}$

**2.** $\begin{cases} 3x + 4y + 2z = 0.5 \\ 8x - 5y - 5z = 8.1 \\ 5x + 5y + 5z = 1 \end{cases}$

**3.** $\begin{cases} 5x - 4y + 3z = -30 \\ 18x - 2y - 19z = 103 \\ 2.9x + 0.06y + 17z = -81.8 \end{cases}$

**4.** $\begin{cases} x + 3y = 5 \\ x + 4y = 6 \end{cases}$

**5.** $\begin{cases} 4x + y + z = 0 \\ 5x + 2y + 3z = -15 \\ 6x - 5y - 5z = 52 \end{cases}$

**6.** $\begin{cases} 2x + 3y = 12 \\ x + 2y = 7 \end{cases}$

**7.** $\begin{cases} x + y + z = 31 \\ x - y + z = 1 \\ x - 2y + 2z = 7 \end{cases}$

**8.** $\begin{cases} x - 3y = -1 \\ -6x + 19y = 6 \end{cases}$

**9.** $\begin{cases} x + y + z = 8.8 \\ 2x - 5y + 9z = -4.8 \\ 3x + 2y - 7z = -7.6 \end{cases}$

**10.** $\begin{cases} -3x + 4y = 2 \\ x - y = -1 \end{cases}$

**11.** $\begin{cases} 0.5x + 1.5y + z = 7 \\ 3x + 3y + 5z = 3 \\ 2x + y + 2z = -1 \end{cases}$

**12.** $\begin{cases} x + y + z = -2 \\ 1.5x + 3y + 0.5z = 8 \\ 9x + 4y + 5z = 4 \end{cases}$

**Write each system as a matrix equation. Identify the coefficient matrix, the variable matrix, and the constant matrix.**

**13.** $\begin{cases} 6x + 9y = 36 \\ 4x + 13y = 2 \end{cases}$

**14.** $\begin{cases} 3x - 4y = -9 \\ 7y = 24 \end{cases}$

**15.** $\begin{cases} 4x - z = 9 \\ 12x + 2y = 17 \\ x - y + 12z = 3 \end{cases}$

**Write a system of equations. Solve the system using an inverse matrix.**

**16.** In 1992, there were 548,303 doctors under the age of 65 in the United States. Of those under age 45, 25.53415% were women. Of those between the ages of 45 and 64, 11.67209% were women. There were 110,017 women doctors under the age of 65. How many doctors were under age 45?

**17.** An apartment building has 50 units. All are one- or two-bedroom units. One-bedroom units rent for $425/mo, and two-bedroom units rent for $550/mo. When all units are occupied, the total monthly income is $25,000. How many apartments of each type are there?

**Solve each matrix equation. If the coefficient matrix has no inverse, write *no unique solution*.**

**18.** $\begin{bmatrix} 0.25 & -0.75 \\ 3.5 & 2.25 \end{bmatrix} \begin{bmatrix} x \\ y \end{bmatrix} = \begin{bmatrix} 1.5 \\ -3.75 \end{bmatrix}$

**19.** $\begin{bmatrix} 3 & -9 \\ 1 & -6 \end{bmatrix} \begin{bmatrix} a \\ b \end{bmatrix} = \begin{bmatrix} 12 \\ 0 \end{bmatrix}$

**20.** $\begin{bmatrix} 3 & -6 \\ -1 & 2 \end{bmatrix} \begin{bmatrix} u \\ v \end{bmatrix} = \begin{bmatrix} 4 \\ 9 \end{bmatrix}$

**21.** $\begin{bmatrix} 12 & -3 \\ 16 & 4 \end{bmatrix} \begin{bmatrix} x \\ y \end{bmatrix} = \begin{bmatrix} 144 \\ -64 \end{bmatrix}$

**Determine whether each system has a unique solution.**

**22.** $\begin{cases} 4d + 2e = 4 \\ d + 3e = 6 \end{cases}$

**23.** $\begin{cases} 3x - 2y = 43 \\ 9x - 6y = 40 \end{cases}$

**24.** $\begin{cases} -y - z = 3 \\ x + 2y + 3z = 1 \\ 4x - 5y - 6z = -50 \end{cases}$

# Practice 4-8

**Write a system of equations for each augmented matrix.**

**1.** $\begin{bmatrix} 4 & -2 & | & 3 \\ 6 & 11 & | & 9 \end{bmatrix}$

**2.** $\begin{bmatrix} 12 & 6 & | & -4 \\ -1 & 0 & | & 2 \end{bmatrix}$

**3.** $\begin{bmatrix} -2 & 9 & -2 & | & 20 \\ 3 & -1 & 2 & | & 29 \\ 6 & 5 & 5 & | & -4 \end{bmatrix}$

**Use Cramer's Rule to solve each system.**

**4.** $\begin{cases} 2x + y = 1 \\ 3x - y = 9 \end{cases}$

**5.** $\begin{cases} 2x - y = 10 \\ x - 3y = 0 \end{cases}$

**6.** $\begin{cases} 3x + 5y = 1 \\ x + 6y = 9 \end{cases}$

**7.** $\begin{cases} x + y + z = 1.28 \\ x - 3y + 2z = 1.26 \\ 3x + 2y + 4z = 4.06 \end{cases}$

**8.** $\begin{cases} 2x + y - z = 0.75 \\ 3x + 3y + 2z = 4 \\ x - 5y + 3z = -2 \end{cases}$

**9.** $\begin{cases} x + y - z = 6 \\ 3x - 9y + z = -2 \\ 0.2x - 0.3y + 0.71z = -1.12 \end{cases}$

**Write an augmented matrix for each system.**

**10.** $\begin{cases} -3x + 4y = -8 \\ 2x - 8y = 16 \end{cases}$

**11.** $\begin{cases} u + 3v = -30 \\ 4u + v = 1 \end{cases}$

**12.** $\begin{cases} x - 4y + z = -9 \\ 3x + 2y - 3z = 9 \\ 4x + 2z = -4 \end{cases}$

**Use an augmented matrix to solve each system.**

**13.** $\begin{cases} x + y + z = 0 \\ 2x - 2y + 3z = 46 \\ 3x + 7y + 11z = 80 \end{cases}$

**14.** $\begin{cases} 3x + y + z = 18 \\ 4x + 2y + 3z = 12 \\ 7x + 8y + 5z = 9 \end{cases}$

**15.** $\begin{cases} 3x + 7y + 10z = 28 \\ 0.7x - 0.6y + 0.8z = 4.3 \\ 12x - 7y - 9z = 77 \end{cases}$

**16.** $\begin{cases} x - 2y - 3z = 2 \\ 2x + y - 5z = 30 \\ 7x - 11y - z = -48 \end{cases}$

**17.** $\begin{cases} x + y + z = 6.5 \\ 3x - 5y + 6z = -35 \\ 5x + 2y + 2z = 10 \end{cases}$

**18.** $\begin{cases} -x + y - z = -2 \\ 3x + 2y + 0.5z = -1.5 \\ 21x + 19y - 2z = -45 \end{cases}$

**Use a graphing calculator to solve each system.**

**19.** $\begin{cases} 4x - 2y + 3z = -2 \\ 2x + 2y + 5z = 16 \\ 8x - 5y - 2z = 4 \end{cases}$

**20.** $\begin{cases} x + y + z = -1 \\ 3x + 5y + 4z = 2 \\ 3x + 6y + 5z = 0 \end{cases}$

**21.** $\begin{cases} x + 3y - 2z = -3 \\ 2x + y - z = -6 \\ 3x - 2y + 4z = 8 \end{cases}$

# Reteaching 4-1

**OBJECTIVE:** Organize data into matrices       **MATERIALS:** Number cube

- The size, or order, of a matrix is specified by its dimensions.
  A $4 \times 9$ matrix has 4 rows and 9 columns.

## Example

Roll the number cube to set up a $4 \times 2$ matrix. Each time, roll twice to produce a two-digit number. Use the left hand first, then the right.

|  | Left | Right |
|---|---|---|
| Trial 1 | 36 | |
| Trial 2 | | |
| Trial 3 | | |
| Trial 4 | | |

←   **Roll the cube twice with your left hand. Suppose these rolls generate a 3 and a 6; in this case, write 36 in row 1.**

|  | Left | Right |
|---|---|---|
| Trial 1 | 36 | |
| Trial 2 | 24 | |
| Trial 3 | 26 | |
| Trial 4 | 55 | |

←   **Repeat, rolling with your left hand to fill in the first column.**

|  | Left | Right |
|---|---|---|
| Trial 1 | 36 | 15 |
| Trial 2 | 24 | 43 |
| Trial 3 | 26 | 22 |
| Trial 4 | 55 | 46 |

←   **Fill the second column for trials 1–4 by rolling with your right hand.**

## Exercises

**Use a number cube to produce the following matrix.**

1. Create a $6 \times 3$ matrix. Label your columns left hand, right hand, and both hands. Let your rows represent six trials.

2. Rewrite the Example matrix as a $2 \times 4$ matrix.

3. Rewrite the matrix in Exercise 1 as a $3 \times 6$ matrix.

# Reteaching 4-2

**OBJECTIVE:** Adding and subtracting matrices          **MATERIALS:** Colored pencils

- To add or subtract matrices of the same size, circle the corresponding entries and their results with the same color pencils.

## Example

Add the two matrices. Use a different color for each set of corresponding entries.

$$\begin{bmatrix} -3 & 5 \\ 9 & -2 \end{bmatrix} + \begin{bmatrix} 7 & -1 \\ 8 & -4 \end{bmatrix} = \qquad \longleftarrow \quad \textbf{Add the corresponding entries.}$$

$$\begin{bmatrix} -3 & 5 \\ 9 & -2 \end{bmatrix} + \begin{bmatrix} 7 & -1 \\ 8 & -4 \end{bmatrix} = \begin{bmatrix} 4 & \\ & \end{bmatrix} \qquad \longleftarrow \quad (-3) + 7 = 4$$

$$\begin{bmatrix} -3 & 5 \\ 9 & -2 \end{bmatrix} + \begin{bmatrix} 7 & -1 \\ 8 & -4 \end{bmatrix} = \begin{bmatrix} 4 & 4 \\ & \end{bmatrix} \qquad \longleftarrow \quad 5 + (-1) = 4$$

$$\begin{bmatrix} -3 & 5 \\ 9 & -2 \end{bmatrix} + \begin{bmatrix} 7 & -1 \\ 8 & -4 \end{bmatrix} = \begin{bmatrix} 4 & 4 \\ 17 & \end{bmatrix} \qquad \longleftarrow \quad 9 + 8 = 17$$

$$\begin{bmatrix} -3 & 5 \\ 9 & -2 \end{bmatrix} + \begin{bmatrix} 7 & -1 \\ 8 & -4 \end{bmatrix} = \begin{bmatrix} 4 & 4 \\ 17 & -6 \end{bmatrix} \qquad \longleftarrow \quad (-2) + (-4) = (-6)$$

## Exercises

**Circle the corresponding entries. Add or subtract the following matrices.**

**1.** $\begin{bmatrix} -3 & 8 \\ 9 & -2 \end{bmatrix} + \begin{bmatrix} 1 & -5 \\ 5 & 0 \end{bmatrix}$

**2.** $\begin{bmatrix} 1 & -2 \\ 0 & -6 \end{bmatrix} - \begin{bmatrix} 6 & -3 \\ -1 & -8 \end{bmatrix}$

**Add or subtract the following matrices.**

**3.** $\begin{bmatrix} 1.5 & 0.5 \\ -2.5 & 2.5 \end{bmatrix} + \begin{bmatrix} -2.5 & -1.5 \\ 3.5 & -4.5 \end{bmatrix}$

**4.** $\begin{bmatrix} 3 & 1 & 4 \\ 0 & 2 & 1 \end{bmatrix} - \begin{bmatrix} 2 & 0 & 5 \\ 3 & 1 & 6 \end{bmatrix}$

**5.** $\begin{bmatrix} -9 & 2 & 0 \\ -1 & 0 & 3 \end{bmatrix} + \begin{bmatrix} -7 & -3 & -4 \\ 8 & -7 & -9 \end{bmatrix}$

**6.** $\begin{bmatrix} 7.5 & 4 \\ 3.5 & 5 \end{bmatrix} - \begin{bmatrix} 3 & -1.5 \\ 0.5 & -6.5 \end{bmatrix}$

**7.** $\begin{bmatrix} -1 & -4 \\ 0 & 5 \\ 9 & 0 \end{bmatrix} + \begin{bmatrix} -8 & -2 \\ 0 & -4 \\ -1 & 5 \end{bmatrix}$

**8.** $\begin{bmatrix} 0 & 1 \\ 5 & 2 \\ -9 & 0 \end{bmatrix} - \begin{bmatrix} -5 & -4 \\ -7 & -2 \\ 8 & 2 \end{bmatrix}$

**9.** $\begin{bmatrix} -2 & 5.5 \\ 9.5 & -4 \\ 0 & 3 \\ -7.5 & 6 \end{bmatrix} - \begin{bmatrix} 7 & -1.5 \\ 6 & 2.5 \\ -1.5 & 3 \\ -4 & 1 \end{bmatrix}$

**10.** $\begin{bmatrix} -4 & 0 & 2 \\ 1 & -7 & -5 \\ 2 & -4 & 9 \end{bmatrix} + \begin{bmatrix} -1 & -3 & 6 \\ 2 & 5 & 1 \\ 5 & -1 & -3 \end{bmatrix}$

# Reteaching 4-3

**Matrix Multiplication**

| **OBJECTIVE:** Multiplying matrices | **MATERIALS:** Two pencils |
|---|---|

- To multiply two matrices, the number of columns in the first matrix must be equal to the number of rows in the second matrix.

- The product matrix has the same number of rows as the first matrix and the same number of columns as the second matrix.

## Example

Find the product $AB$.

$$AB = \begin{bmatrix} 3 & 1 & -1 \\ 2 & 0 & 3 \end{bmatrix} \begin{bmatrix} 1 & 4 \\ 3 & -1 \\ 2 & 5 \end{bmatrix}$$

**Step 1: Check dimensions of matrices $A$ and $B$ to determine whether they can be multiplied. $A$ has three columns and $B$ has three rows.**

$(3)(1) + (1)(3) + (-1)(2) = 4$

$\begin{bmatrix} 4 & \\ & \end{bmatrix}$

**Step 2: Use two pencils to cover the second row of $A$ and the second column of $B$ so that only the first row of $A$ and the first column of $B$ can be seen. Multiply corresponding elements, and add the products. Place the result at $(AB)_{11}$.**

$(3)(4) + (1)(-1) + (-1)(5) = 6$

$\begin{bmatrix} 4 & 6 \\ & \end{bmatrix}$

**Step 3: Find $(AB)_{12}$ by multiplying the first row of $A$ by the second column of $B$. Add the products, and enter the result. With your pencils, cover the rows and columns that you are not multiplying.**

$(2)(1) + (0)(3) + (3)(2) = 8$

$\begin{bmatrix} 4 & 6 \\ 8 & \end{bmatrix}$

**Step 4: Find $(AB)_{21}$ by multiplying the second row of $A$ by the first column of $B$. Add the products, and enter the result.**

$(2)(4) + (0)(-1) + (3)(5) = 23$

$\begin{bmatrix} 4 & 6 \\ 8 & 23 \end{bmatrix}$

**Step 5: Find $(AB)_{22}$ by multiplying the second row of $A$ by the second column of $B$. Add the products, and enter the result.**

## Exercises

**Multiply the matrices.**

**1.** $\begin{bmatrix} 1 & 2 \\ 4 & 3 \end{bmatrix} \begin{bmatrix} -3 & 5 \\ 2 & -1 \end{bmatrix}$

**2.** $\begin{bmatrix} 4 & 1 & 2 \\ -3 & 2 & 3 \\ 2 & 0 & 5 \\ 3 & 1 & 4 \end{bmatrix} \begin{bmatrix} 1 & 4 \\ 2 & 0 \\ -3 & 5 \end{bmatrix}$

**3.** $\begin{bmatrix} 4 & 1 & 0 & 2 \end{bmatrix} \begin{bmatrix} 1 & 0 & 1 \\ 2 & -1 & 0 \\ 3 & 5 & 1 \\ 1 & 3 & 0 \end{bmatrix}$

# Reteaching 4-4

**OBJECTIVE:** Representing translations with matrices

**MATERIALS:** Graph paper and colored pencils

- A *translation* is a transformation that changes the location of a geometrical figure.

## Example

A quadrilateral has vertices $A(0, 0)$, $B(-2, 3)$, $C(-5, 3)$, and $D(-5, 0)$. Use a matrix to translate the vertices 5 units right and 3 units down.

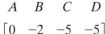

$$\begin{bmatrix} 0 & -2 & -5 & -5 \\ 0 & 3 & 3 & 0 \end{bmatrix}$$

⟵ **Write the vertices as a matrix.**

$$\begin{bmatrix} 5 & 5 & 5 & 5 \\ -3 & -3 & -3 & -3 \end{bmatrix}$$

⟵ **Write the translation matrix. Since the first row represents the *x*-coordinates, place 5 in each entry. Since the second row represents the *y*-coordinates, place $-3$ in each entry.**

$$\begin{bmatrix} 0 & -2 & -5 & -5 \\ 0 & 3 & 3 & 0 \end{bmatrix} + \begin{bmatrix} 5 & 5 & 5 & 5 \\ -3 & -3 & -3 & -3 \end{bmatrix}$$

⟵ **Add the two matrices. Draw arrows connecting corresponding entries. Use a different colored pencil for each arrow.**

$$\begin{matrix} A' & B' & C' & D' \\ \end{matrix}$$
$$= \begin{bmatrix} 5 & 3 & 0 & 0 \\ -3 & 0 & 0 & -3 \end{bmatrix}$$

⟵ **Represent the translated points by A′, B′, C′, and D′ respectively.**

$A'(5, -3)$, $B'(3, 0)$, $C'(0, 0)$, $D'(0, -3)$

⟵ **Write the vertices as ordered pairs.**

⟵ **Graph the original figure and its image. Label each point.**

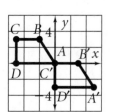

## Exercises

A quadrilateral has vertices $A(0, 0)$, $B(-2, 3)$, $C(1, 4)$, and $D(3, 2)$. Use a matrix to translate the vertices according to the following. Graph the original figure and the image on graph paper.

**1.** a translation 1 unit right and 2 units down

**2.** a translation 3 units left and 1 unit down

**3.** a translation 4 units left and 3 units up

**4.** a translation 2 units right and 4 units up

# Reteaching 4-5

**2 × 2 Matrices, Determinants, and Inverses**

**OBJECTIVE:** Finding and using the inverse of a 2 × 2 matrix

**MATERIALS:** None

- The inverse of a matrix $A$ is the matrix $A^{-1}$ such that the product $AA^{-1} = I$, the identity matrix. Suppose $A = \begin{bmatrix} a & b \\ c & d \end{bmatrix}$. If $ad - bc \neq 0$, then $A$ has an inverse and $A^{-1} = \dfrac{1}{ad - bc} \begin{bmatrix} d & -b \\ -c & a \end{bmatrix}$.

## Example

Write the inverse of the matrix $A = \begin{bmatrix} 2 & 4 \\ 1 & 3 \end{bmatrix}$.

$ad - bc = (2)(3) - (4)(1)$
$\qquad\quad 2 \neq 0$
⟵ **Calculate $ad - bc$. Since $ad - bc \neq 0$, the inverse does exist.**

$A^{-1} = \dfrac{1}{2} \begin{bmatrix} 3 & -4 \\ -1 & 2 \end{bmatrix}$
⟵ **Substitute values into the matrix inverse formula.**

$= \begin{bmatrix} \dfrac{3}{2} & -2 \\ -\dfrac{1}{2} & 1 \end{bmatrix}$
⟵ **Multiply each entry by $\frac{1}{2}$.**

$\quad A \qquad\qquad A^{-1} \qquad\qquad I$

$\begin{bmatrix} 2 & 4 \\ 1 & 3 \end{bmatrix} \begin{bmatrix} \dfrac{3}{2} & -2 \\ -\dfrac{1}{2} & 1 \end{bmatrix} = \begin{bmatrix} 1 & 0 \\ 0 & 1 \end{bmatrix}$
⟵ **Check the results by verifying that $AA^{-1} = I$.**

because

$\begin{bmatrix} 2\left(\dfrac{3}{2}\right) + 4\left(-\dfrac{1}{2}\right) & 2(-2) + 4(1) \\ 1\left(\dfrac{3}{2}\right) + 3\left(-\dfrac{1}{2}\right) & 1(-2) + 3(1) \end{bmatrix} = \begin{bmatrix} 1 & 0 \\ 0 & 1 \end{bmatrix}$
⟵ **Multiply each row of A by each column of $A^{-1}$ to calculate the product of A and $A^{-1}$.**

## Exercises

**Find the inverse of each 2 × 2 matrix. If it does not exist, write *no inverse*.**

**1.** $\begin{bmatrix} 5 & -2 \\ -7 & 3 \end{bmatrix}$

**2.** $\begin{bmatrix} 9 & -2 \\ 5 & -1 \end{bmatrix}$

**3.** $\begin{bmatrix} 3 & 4 \\ 5 & 7 \end{bmatrix}$

**4.** $\begin{bmatrix} 6 & -3 \\ -2 & 1 \end{bmatrix}$

**5.** $\begin{bmatrix} -2 & 17 \\ 1 & 8 \end{bmatrix}$

**6.** $\begin{bmatrix} 7 & 4 \\ 3 & 2 \end{bmatrix}$

**7.** $\begin{bmatrix} 7 & -3 \\ -1 & 1 \end{bmatrix}$

**8.** $\begin{bmatrix} -9 & 3 \\ 6 & -2 \end{bmatrix}$

**9.** $\begin{bmatrix} 3 & 4 \\ 5 & 6 \end{bmatrix}$

# Reteaching 4-6

**OBJECTIVE:** Finding the determinant of a 3 × 3 matrix

**MATERIALS:** Colored Pencils

Like 2 × 2 matrices, a 3 × 3 matrix, $A = \begin{bmatrix} a_1 & b_1 & c_1 \\ a_2 & b_2 & c_2 \\ a_3 & b_3 & c_3 \end{bmatrix}$, has a determinant, det A.

$\det A = (a_1 b_2 c_3 + a_2 b_3 c_1 + a_3 b_1 c_2) - (a_1 b_3 c_2 + a_2 b_1 c_3 + a_3 b_2 c_1)$

Write matrix $A$, then copy matrix $A$ to the right of the first matrix, aligning rows. In your first matrix, use three colored pencils and the first part of the formula to show what is being multiplied. In the second matrix, use other colors and the second part of the formula to show what is being multiplied. Do you see a pattern? This pattern will help you calculate the determinant of $A$.

## Example

Find the determinant of $A$ if $A = \begin{bmatrix} 3 & 2 & 1 \\ 4 & 3 & -2 \\ 5 & 0 & 0 \end{bmatrix}$.

$\det A = [3(3)(0) + 4(0)(1) + 5(2)(-2)]$  ⟵ **Use the definition.**
$\quad\quad - [3(0)(-2) + 4(2)(0) + 5(3)(1)]$

$\quad = [0 + 0 + -20] - [0 + 0 + 15]$  ⟵ **Multiply.**

$\quad = -20 - 15 = -35$  ⟵ **Simplify.**

## Exercises

**Evaluate the determinant of each matrix.**

**1.** $\begin{bmatrix} 1 & -1 & -1 \\ -2 & 0 & 1 \\ 1 & -1 & 2 \end{bmatrix}$
**2.** $\begin{bmatrix} 0 & 1 & 2 \\ 3 & 2 & 1 \\ 4 & 0 & 3 \end{bmatrix}$
**3.** $\begin{bmatrix} 1 & 0 & 3 \\ 4 & 2 & -1 \\ -1 & 0 & 4 \end{bmatrix}$

**4.** $\begin{bmatrix} 3 & 1 & 12 \\ -2 & 0 & -6 \\ 3 & 5 & -1 \end{bmatrix}$
**5.** $\begin{bmatrix} 1 & 2 & -2 \\ -1 & 3 & 1 \\ 1 & -1 & 2 \end{bmatrix}$
**6.** $\begin{bmatrix} 1 & 2 & 3 \\ -4 & 5 & -4 \\ 2 & 6 & 7 \end{bmatrix}$

# Reteaching 4-7

**Inverse Matrices and Systems**

**OBJECTIVE:** Solving systems using inverse matrices

**MATERIALS:** Graphing calculator

- A system of linear equations can be solved by using inverse matrices when the system has exactly one solution.

- The determinant of $\begin{bmatrix} a & b \\ c & d \end{bmatrix}$ is $ad - bc$.

- If the determinant is zero, the matrix has no inverse.

- If the determinant is zero, the matrix equation has no solution or an infinite number of solutions. To solve, use another method.

## Example

Use an inverse matrix to solve the linear system $\begin{cases} 4x + 3y = -4 \\ 3x - y = -3 \end{cases}$.

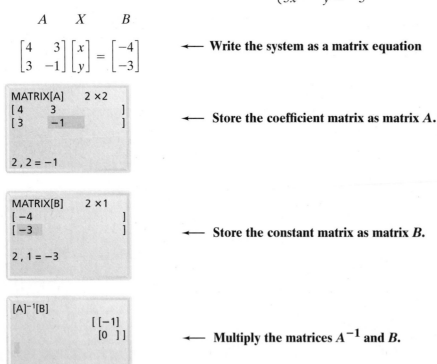

$$\begin{matrix} A & X & B \end{matrix}$$

$$\begin{bmatrix} 4 & 3 \\ 3 & -1 \end{bmatrix} \begin{bmatrix} x \\ y \end{bmatrix} = \begin{bmatrix} -4 \\ -3 \end{bmatrix}$$

◀── **Write the system as a matrix equation**

```
MATRIX[A]    2 ×2
[ 4      3         ]
[ 3      −1        ]

2 , 2 = −1
```

◀── **Store the coefficient matrix as matrix $A$.**

```
MATRIX[B]    2 ×1
[ −4              ]
[ −3              ]

2 , 1 = −3
```

◀── **Store the constant matrix as matrix $B$.**

```
[A]⁻¹[B]
             [ [−1]
               [0  ] ]

```

◀── **Multiply the matrices $A^{-1}$ and $B$.**

Check the solution $(-1, 0)$ by substitution.

## Exercises

**Use a graphing calculator to solve each system. Check your solutions by substitution.**

**1.** $\begin{cases} 2x - 7y = -3 \\ x + 5y = 7 \end{cases}$  **2.** $\begin{cases} x + 3y = 5 \\ x + 4y = 6 \end{cases}$  **3.** $\begin{cases} p - 3q = -1 \\ -5p + 16q = 5 \end{cases}$  **4.** $\begin{cases} 4m - 2n = -6 \\ -2m + n = 3 \end{cases}$

# Reteaching 4-8

**OBJECTIVE:** Using the augmented matrix to solve systems of equations

**MATERIALS:** None

Remember the row operations:

- Switch any two rows.

- Multiply a row by a constant.

- Add one row to another.

- Combine one or more of these steps.

## Example

Use an augmented matrix to solve the system $\begin{cases} 2x + 4y = 8 \\ 3x + 5y = 15 \end{cases}$.

After the row operations, you want the system to be in the form $\begin{bmatrix} 1 & 0 & | & m \\ 0 & 1 & | & n \end{bmatrix}$.
The solution to the system is $(m, n)$.

**Write the augmented matrix.**
$\longrightarrow \begin{bmatrix} 2 & 4 & | & 8 \\ 3 & 5 & | & 15 \end{bmatrix}$

**To make element $a_{11}$ equal to 1, multiply Row 1 by $\frac{1}{2}$.**
**Then replace Row 1 with the result.**
$\frac{1}{2}(2 \ \ 4 \ \ 8) = (1 \ \ 2 \ \ 4) \quad \longrightarrow \begin{bmatrix} 1 & 2 & | & 4 \\ 3 & 5 & | & 15 \end{bmatrix}$

**To make element $a_{21}$ equal to 0, multiply Row 1**
**by $-3$. Then add the result to Row 2, and replace**
**Row 2 with this sum.**

$$
\begin{array}{rrr}
-3(1 \ \ 2 \ \ 4) & = & (-3 \ -6 \ -12) \\
-3 & -6 & -12 \\
3 & 5 & 15 \\
\hline
0 & -1 & 3
\end{array}
\longrightarrow \begin{bmatrix} 1 & 2 & | & 4 \\ 0 & -1 & | & 3 \end{bmatrix}
$$

**To make element $a_{22}$ equal to 1, multiply Row 2**
**by $-1$. Then replace Row 2 with the result.**
$-1(0 \ -1 \ \ 3) = (0 \ \ 1 \ -3) \quad \longrightarrow \begin{bmatrix} 1 & 2 & | & 4 \\ 0 & 1 & | & -3 \end{bmatrix}$

**To make element $a_{12}$ equal to 0, multiply Row 2**
**by $-2$. Then add the result to Row 1, and replace**
**Row 1 with this sum.**

$$
\begin{array}{rrr}
-2(0 \ \ 1 \ -3) & = & (0 \ -2 \ \ 6) \\
0 & -2 & 6 \\
1 & 2 & 4 \\
\hline
1 & 0 & 10
\end{array}
\longrightarrow \begin{bmatrix} 1 & 0 & | & 10 \\ 0 & 1 & | & -3 \end{bmatrix}
$$

The solution to the system is $(10, -3)$. You can check the solution by

substituting $x = 10$ and $y = -3$ into each of the original equations.

## Exercises

**1.** $\begin{cases} x - 5y = 4 \\ -2x + y = 1 \end{cases}$

**2.** $\begin{cases} x - 3y = 5 \\ 3x - y = -1 \end{cases}$

**3.** $\begin{cases} 2x - y = 6 \\ 3x - y = 2 \end{cases}$

# Enrichment 4-1

## *Brain Teaser*

Find a quote by Albert Einstein. Use the matrix of letters to fill in the blanks with the corresponding matrix element.

$\overline{\phantom{x}}_{a_{48}}$  $\overline{\phantom{x}}_{a_{32}}\ \overline{\phantom{x}}_{a_{18}}\ \overline{\phantom{x}}_{a_{19}}\ \overline{\phantom{x}}_{a_{25}}\ \overline{\phantom{x}}_{a_{22}}$  $\overline{\phantom{x}}_{a_{11}}\ \overline{\phantom{x}}_{a_{25}}\ \overline{\phantom{x}}_{a_{14}}$  $\overline{\phantom{x}}_{a_{32}}\ \overline{\phantom{x}}_{a_{18}}\ \overline{\phantom{x}}_{a_{19}}\ \overline{\phantom{x}}_{a_{25}}\ \overline{\phantom{x}}_{a_{22}}$  $\overline{\phantom{x}}_{a_{16}}\ \overline{\phantom{x}}_{a_{26}}\ \overline{\phantom{x}}_{a_{29}}$

$\overline{\phantom{x}}_{a_{24}}\ \overline{\phantom{x}}_{a_{26}}\ \overline{\phantom{x}}_{a_{25}}\ \overline{\phantom{x}}_{a_{32}}\ \overline{\phantom{x}}_{a_{18}}\ \overline{\phantom{x}}_{a_{31}}$  $\overline{\phantom{x}}_{a_{11}}\ \overline{\phantom{x}}_{a_{25}}\ \overline{\phantom{x}}_{a_{14}}$  $\overline{\phantom{x}}_{a_{37}}\ \overline{\phantom{x}}_{a_{15}}\ \overline{\phantom{x}}_{a_{11}}\ \overline{\phantom{x}}_{a_{29}}\ \overline{\phantom{x}}_{a_{31}}$ .

$\overline{\phantom{x}}_{a_{54}}\ \overline{\phantom{x}}_{a_{19}}\ \overline{\phantom{x}}_{a_{25}}\ \overline{\phantom{x}}_{a_{15}}\ \overline{\phantom{x}}_{a_{32}}\ \overline{\phantom{x}}_{a_{37}}$ - $\overline{\phantom{x}}_{a_{25}}\ \overline{\phantom{x}}_{a_{19}}\ \overline{\phantom{x}}_{a_{25}}\ \overline{\phantom{x}}_{a_{15}}$  $\overline{\phantom{x}}_{a_{32}}\ \overline{\phantom{x}}_{a_{19}}\ \overline{\phantom{x}}_{a_{24}}\ \overline{\phantom{x}}_{a_{15}}\ \overline{\phantom{x}}_{a_{31}}$ ,  $\overline{\phantom{x}}_{a_{32}}\ \overline{\phantom{x}}_{a_{18}}\ \overline{\phantom{x}}_{a_{15}}$

$\overline{\phantom{x}}_{a_{13}}\ \overline{\phantom{x}}_{a_{26}}\ \overline{\phantom{x}}_{a_{25}}\ \overline{\phantom{x}}_{a_{13}}\ \overline{\phantom{x}}_{a_{23}}\ \overline{\phantom{x}}_{a_{33}}\ \overline{\phantom{x}}_{a_{31}}\ \overline{\phantom{x}}_{a_{19}}\ \overline{\phantom{x}}_{a_{26}}\ \overline{\phantom{x}}_{a_{25}}$  $\overline{\phantom{x}}_{a_{19}}\ \overline{\phantom{x}}_{a_{31}}$  $\overline{\phantom{x}}_{a_{16}}\ \overline{\phantom{x}}_{a_{11}}\ \overline{\phantom{x}}_{a_{23}}\ \overline{\phantom{x}}_{a_{31}}\ \overline{\phantom{x}}_{a_{15}}$ .

$\overline{\phantom{x}}_{a_{61}}\ \overline{\phantom{x}}_{a_{18}}\ \overline{\phantom{x}}_{a_{15}}$  $\overline{\phantom{x}}_{a_{18}}\ \overline{\phantom{x}}_{a_{33}}\ \overline{\phantom{x}}_{a_{25}}\ \overline{\phantom{x}}_{a_{14}}\ \overline{\phantom{x}}_{a_{29}}\ \overline{\phantom{x}}_{a_{15}}\ \overline{\phantom{x}}_{a_{14}}\ \overline{\phantom{x}}_{a_{32}}\ \overline{\phantom{x}}_{a_{18}}$  $\overline{\phantom{x}}_{a_{32}}\ \overline{\phantom{x}}_{a_{19}}\ \overline{\phantom{x}}_{a_{24}}\ \overline{\phantom{x}}_{a_{15}}$  $\overline{\phantom{x}}_{a_{48}}$

$\overline{\phantom{x}}_{a_{11}}\ \overline{\phantom{x}}_{a_{24}}$  $\overline{\phantom{x}}_{a_{29}}\ \overline{\phantom{x}}_{a_{19}}\ \overline{\phantom{x}}_{a_{17}}\ \overline{\phantom{x}}_{a_{18}}\ \overline{\phantom{x}}_{a_{32}}$ .

**— Albert Einstein**

$$A = \begin{bmatrix} a & b & c & d & e & f & g & h & i \\ j & k & l & m & n & o & p & q & r \\ s & t & u & v & w & x & y & z & A \\ B & C & D & E & F & G & H & I & J \\ K & L & M & N & O & P & Q & R & S \\ T & U & V & W & X & Y & Z & ! & ? \end{bmatrix}$$

# Enrichment 4-2

*A Mathematical City*

Fill in the blanks to find an American city named for a famous mathematician. Complete each matrix calculation. When you find a 0 in the resulting matrix, note the row and column numbers. Then, *reverse* the row and column numbers. The matrix element in this position indicates where to place the corresponding letter.

$$\overline{1} \quad \overline{2} \quad \overline{3} \quad \overline{4} \quad \overline{5} \quad \overline{6} \quad \overline{7} \quad \overline{8} \quad \overline{9} \quad \overline{10} \quad \overline{11}$$

**L**
$$\begin{bmatrix} 5 & 6 \\ 8 & -3 \\ 0 & 2 \end{bmatrix} - \begin{bmatrix} 2 & 6 \\ 4 & 4 \\ -2 & 10 \end{bmatrix}$$

**O**
$$\begin{bmatrix} 0 & -1 & 2 \\ -2 & 4 & 1 \\ -3 & 0 & 3 \end{bmatrix} + \begin{bmatrix} 1 & 6 & 9 \\ 1 & 0 & 5 \\ 3 & 3 & 2 \end{bmatrix}$$

**D**
$$\begin{bmatrix} 1 & -6 & 0 \\ 6 & 5 & 5 \end{bmatrix} - \begin{bmatrix} 2 & -12 & 2 \\ 6 & -5 & 7 \end{bmatrix}$$

**O**
$$\begin{bmatrix} 1 & -2 & 3 & 5 \\ 3 & 1 & -1 & 8 \\ 4 & 2 & 7 & -7 \end{bmatrix} + \begin{bmatrix} 2 & -4 & 5 & 0 \\ -1 & 3 & 5 & -6 \\ -4 & -5 & 4 & 3 \end{bmatrix}$$

**E**
$$\begin{bmatrix} -3 & -5 & 6 & 7 \\ 2 & 6 & 1 & -4 \\ 3 & 4 & -5 & -6 \end{bmatrix} - \begin{bmatrix} 1 & -2 & 6 & 5 \\ -3 & 1 & -1 & -3 \\ 2 & 3 & 1 & 0 \end{bmatrix}$$

**I**
$$\begin{bmatrix} 1 & -3 & 8 \\ 3 & -4 & 0 \\ 12 & 7 & 3 \end{bmatrix} - \begin{bmatrix} 2 & -1 & 8 \\ 2 & -3 & 1 \\ 2 & 9 & 4 \end{bmatrix}$$

**C**
$$\begin{bmatrix} 1 & 2 & 3 & 1 & 8 \\ 4 & 1 & 6 & 2 & 8 \\ -3 & 8 & -7 & 3 & -4 \end{bmatrix} + \begin{bmatrix} 3 & -4 & -7 & -4 & -1 \\ 3 & 0 & -6 & -5 & 2 \\ 5 & -5 & 4 & -2 & 5 \end{bmatrix}$$

**H**
$$\begin{bmatrix} 3 & 5 & -6 & 7 \\ 8 & -5 & 6 & 2 \\ 1 & 5 & 0 & 6 \end{bmatrix} + \begin{bmatrix} 1 & -2 & -1 & -3 \\ -5 & 3 & -6 & -4 \\ 3 & 4 & -3 & 0 \end{bmatrix}$$

**U**
$$\begin{bmatrix} 2 & -8 & 3 \\ 7 & 3 & 3 \\ 1 & 6 & 5 \end{bmatrix} - \begin{bmatrix} 4 & -9 & 0 \\ 14 & 5 & 1 \\ -4 & 6 & 8 \end{bmatrix}$$

**I**
$$\begin{bmatrix} 1 & 3 & 8 & -5 \\ 6 & -2 & 0 & 5 \\ 9 & -3 & 4 & 7 \end{bmatrix} - \begin{bmatrix} 2 & -2 & 8 & -1 \\ 4 & 3 & 1 & 0 \\ 4 & 1 & 1 & 5 \end{bmatrix}$$

# Enrichment 4-3

## Nilpotent Matrices

A matrix $A$ is said to be nilpotent if there is an integer $n$ such that $A^n = 0$, the zero matrix.

1. What can you say about the dimensions of a nilpotent matrix? Why?

   If $A = \begin{bmatrix} 0 & 1 \\ 0 & 0 \end{bmatrix}$, find $A^2$ and $A^3$.

   What can you conclude?

The *order* of a nilpotent matrix $A$ is the least integer $n$ such that $A^n = 0$. In the example above, although both $A^2 = 0$ and $A^3 = 0$, the order of matrix $A$ is 2.

2. Examine the conditions under which a nonzero $2 \times 2$ matrix of order 2 is nilpotent. Suppose

   $A = \begin{bmatrix} a & b \\ c & d \end{bmatrix}$. Find $A^2$.

If $A$ is nilpotent of order 2, then $A^2 = 0$. Therefore, each element of the matrix $A^2$ must be equal to zero.

3. Write four equations which show that the elements in the corresponding rows and columns are zero.

   Equation (1, 1):                 Equation (1, 2):

   Equation (2, 1):                 Equation (2, 2):

4. Factor equation (1, 2).

5. Find two possible solutions.

6. If $b = 0$, what can you conclude from equation (1, 1)?

   From equation (2, 2)?

7. Use this information to write matrix $A$. Verify that this matrix is nilpotent of order 2.

8. Using equations (2, 1), (1, 1), and (2, 2), and substituting in matrix $A$, find another nilpotent matrix of order 2.

# Enrichment 4-4

*Transformations*

Find the coordinates of the image under each transformation. On the same
coordinate plane, graph and then shade each quadrilateral to reveal a word.

$\begin{bmatrix} 0 & 1 & 3 & 2 \\ 4 & 4 & 0 & 0 \end{bmatrix}$; a translation 1 unit left and 3 units up

$\begin{bmatrix} -2 & -3 & -1 & 0 \\ -3 & -3 & -7 & -7 \end{bmatrix}$; a reflection in the *x*-axis

$\begin{bmatrix} 4 & 5 & 5 & 4 \\ 0 & 0 & 2 & 2 \end{bmatrix}$; a rotation of 90°

$\begin{bmatrix} 6 & 7 & 7 & 6 \\ 3 & 3 & 7 & 7 \end{bmatrix}$; a rotation of 360°

$\begin{bmatrix} 7 & 8 & 8 & 7 \\ -4 & -4 & -5 & -5 \end{bmatrix}$; a reflection in the *x*-axis

$\begin{bmatrix} -8 & -9 & -9 & -8 \\ -3 & -3 & -7 & -7 \end{bmatrix}$; a rotation of 180°

$\begin{bmatrix} 5 & 4 & 4 & 5 \\ 3 & 3 & 7 & 7 \end{bmatrix}$; a reflection in the *y*-axis

$\begin{bmatrix} -5 & -5 & -7 & -7 \\ -7 & -6 & -4 & -5 \end{bmatrix}$; a rotation of 270°

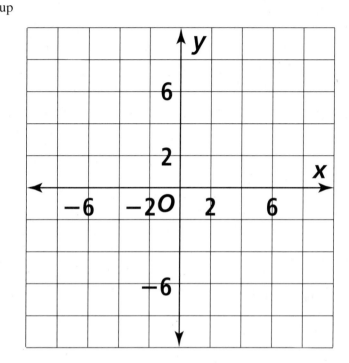

$\begin{bmatrix} 1 & 2 & 4 & 3 \\ 8 & 8 & 6 & 6 \end{bmatrix}$; a translation 10 units left and 1 unit down

$\begin{bmatrix} -1 & 2 & 2 & -1 \\ 3 & 3 & 2 & 2 \end{bmatrix}$; a translation 3 units right and 4 units up

$\begin{bmatrix} 6 & 6 & 3 & 3 \\ 3 & 4 & 4 & 3 \end{bmatrix}$; a reflection in *y* = *x*

$\begin{bmatrix} -3 & -3 & -7 & -7 \\ 9 & 8 & 8 & 9 \end{bmatrix}$; a reflection in *y* = −*x*

# Enrichment 4-5

•••••••••••••••••••••••••••••••••••••••••••••••••••••••••••••
*Determinants, Products, and Inverses*

Suppose $A$ and $B$ are $2 \times 2$ matrices as follows:

$$A = \begin{bmatrix} a & b \\ c & d \end{bmatrix}, \qquad B = \begin{bmatrix} e & f \\ g & h \end{bmatrix}$$

1. What is the value of the determinant of $A$, det $A$?

2. Evaluate det $B$.

3. Evaluate det $A \cdot$ det $B$.

4. Compute matrix $AB$.

5. Evaluate det($AB$).

6. What can you conclude?

7. Explain your results.

8. Suppose that a $2 \times 2$ matrix $A$ has an inverse $A^{-1}$. Use the product rule to investigate how the determinant of $A^{-1}$ is related to the determinant of $A$.

   $\det(A \cdot A^{-1}) = \det A \cdot \det A^{-1}$

   _____ $= \det A \cdot \det A^{-1}$

   _____ $= \det A \cdot \det A^{-1}$

   _____ $= \det A^{-1}$

9. Explain your results.

# Enrichment 4-6

••••••••••••••••••••••••••••••••••••••••••••••••••••••••••••••••••
## *Determinants of 3 × 3 and 4 × 4 Matrices*

The determinant of a $3 \times 3$ matrix $\begin{bmatrix} a_1 & b_1 & c_1 \\ a_2 & b_2 & c_2 \\ a_3 & b_3 & c_3 \end{bmatrix}$ can be found by using submatrices that are formed by removing rows and columns.

The submatrix $M_{ij}$ is formed by removing the $i$th row and the $j$th column.

For example, $M_{12}$ is the submatrix formed by removing the first row and the second column.

$$\begin{bmatrix} a_1 & b_1 & c_1 \\ a_2 & b_2 & c_2 \\ a_3 & b_3 & c_3 \end{bmatrix}$$

So $M_{12} = \begin{bmatrix} a_2 & c_2 \\ a_3 & c_3 \end{bmatrix}$.

The determinant of a $3 \times 3$ matrix $A$ is $\det A = a_1 \det M_{11} - b_1 \det M_{12} + c_1 \det M_{13}$.

**1.** Verify that $\det A = a_1 \det M_{11} - b_1 \det M_{12} + c_1 \det M_{13}$ gives the formula shown in your textbook.

The determinant of a $4 \times 4$ matrix $A$ can be found in a similar manner:

$$\det A = a_1 \det M_{11} - b_1 \det M_{12} + c_1 \det M_{13} - d_1 \det M_{14}$$

**2.** Find the determinant of $B = \begin{bmatrix} 1 & 2 & 3 & 4 \\ 0 & 1 & 2 & 3 \\ 4 & 0 & 1 & 2 \\ 3 & 4 & 0 & 1 \end{bmatrix}$ using the formula above.

**3.** The matrix $A = \begin{bmatrix} 1 & 2 & 3 & 4 \\ 1 & 2 & 3 & 4 \\ 4 & 5 & 6 & 7 \\ 3 & 4 & 5 & 6 \end{bmatrix}$ has two identical rows. Calculate $\det A$.

**4.** Write a $3 \times 3$ matrix with two identical rows. Calculate its determinant.

**5.** Write a $2 \times 2$ matrix with two identical rows. Calculate its determinant.

**6.** What do you think the determinant of an $n \times n$ matrix with two identical rows will be?

# Enrichment 4-7

• • • • • • • • • • • • • • • • • • • • • • • • • • • • • • • • • • • • • • • • • • • • • • • • • • • • • • • • • • • • • •

*Food for Thought*

For each of the following problems, write a system of three equations in three unknowns, and solve for the quantity of food needed using inverse matrices.

1. A delicatessen delivers a gigantic sandwich to be shared by the 12 members of a jury who have been unable to reach a verdict. The sandwich consists of bread, meat, and cheese. The cost of the sandwich is \$.60/lb for the bread, \$3.00/lb for the meat, and \$1.50/lb for the cheese. One pound of bread supplies 10 g of protein, one pound of meat supplies 50 g of protein, and a pound of cheese supplies 40 g of protein. Each member of the jury pays \$1.50 for a one-pound portion of the sandwich. Each one-pound portion contains 30 g of protein. How much of each ingredient is in the whole sandwich?

2. Paella is a classic Spanish fiesta dish made from chicken, rice, and shellfish. One pound of chicken costs \$1.00 and supplies 100 g of protein. One pound of rice costs \$.50 and supplies 20 g of protein. One pound of shellfish costs \$3.00 and supplies 50 g of protein. If the resulting paella weighs 18 lb, costs \$19.00, and supplies 850 g of protein, how much rice, chicken, and shellfish were used?

3. The local yogurt bar features a banana treat made up of 2 lb of bananas, 3 lb of topping, and 4 lb of frozen yogurt. The cost of the banana treat is \$19.00. One pound of topping costs \$1 less than one pound of frozen yogurt, which costs as much as $\frac{1}{2}$ lb of topping and 4 lb of bananas. How much does one pound of each ingredient cost?

4. The banana treat in Exercise 3 contains 5400 calories. There are half as many calories in one pound of frozen yogurt as there are in one pound of topping. Together, 2 lb of frozen yogurt and 5 lb of bananas have the same amount of calories as 2 lb of topping. Find the number of calories in one pound of each of the items.

# Enrichment 4-8
••••••••••••••••••••••••••••••••••••••••••••••••••••••••••••••••••••
## *Well-Conditioned Systems of Linear Equations*

A system of linear equations is said to be well-conditioned if a small change in the values of the coefficients produces a small change in the values of the solutions. A system is said to be ill-conditioned if a small change in the values of the coefficients produces a large change in the values of the solutions.

To determine whether a system of linear equations is well-conditioned or ill-conditioned, change each coefficient by one percent. Each time, write and solve the new system, finding the values of $x$ and $y$ to two decimal places using Cramer's Rule. Then compare the new values of $x$ and $y$ to the solutions of the original system. A change of less than one percent in the values of $x$ and $y$ can be considered small.

1. Determine whether System 1 is well-conditioned or ill-conditioned by completing the following steps.

   System 1: $\begin{cases} x + y = 5000 \\ 3x - 2y = 3000 \end{cases}$

   a. Find the values of $x$ and $y$.

   b. Change the coefficient of $x$ in the first equation by one percent, from 1 to 1.01. Write the new system. Find the values of $x$ and $y$.

   c. Change the coefficient of $y$ in the first equation by one percent, from 1 to 0.99. Write the new system. Find the values of $x$ and $y$.

   d. Change the coefficient of $x$ in the second equation by one percent, from 3 to 3.03. Write the new system. Find the values of $x$ and $y$.

   e. Change the coefficient of $y$ in the second equation by one percent, from $-2$ to $-2.02$. Write the new system. Find the values of $x$ and $y$.

   f. Is the system well-conditioned or ill-conditioned?

2. Determine whether System 2 is well-conditioned or ill-conditioned by completing the same steps as in Exercise 1.

   System 2: $\begin{cases} x + y = 5001 \\ 3x - 2y = -9997 \end{cases}$

# Chapter 4 Project: Munching Microbes

## *Beginning the Chapter Project*

Oil spills and chemical contamination of groundwater are some of the present-day hazards. The field of bioremediation uses bacteria that occur naturally in the environment to decompose hazardous wastes.

In this project, you will organize data from a bioremediation project. You will manipulate the data and use the results to draw conclusions and make predictions. Then you will research other bioremediation projects. Finally, you will summarize and display your findings.

**List of Materials**

- Calculator

- Graph paper

- Poster board

## *Activities*

### Activity 1: Organizing
The table shows data from an above-ground biotreatment project. Scientists analyzed five samples from the same soil for the presence of hazardous components of petroleum products. They found benzene (B), toluene (T), ethylbenzene (E), and xylene (X).

- Present the data in four matrices.

- Choose an element from each matrix and tell what it represents.

### Activity 2: Calculating
In this activity, you will use the matrices you wrote for Activity 1.

- Use matrices to find the combined amount of benzene, toluene, ethylbenzene, and xylene in mg/kg for each soil sample.

- After 12 months of bioremediation, the levels of each component dropped to less than 0.05 mg/kg for each soil sample. Use matrices to calculate the minimum amount by which the level of each component for each sample dropped.

**Component Levels in Soil (mg/kg)**

| Sample | B | T | E | X |
|--------|------|------|------|------|
| 1 | 0.06 | 0.95 | 0.9 | 18.5 |
| 2 | 0.06 | 1.05 | 0.73 | 13.5 |
| 3 | 0.35 | 6 | 5.6 | 49 |
| 4 | 0.22 | 0.19 | 2 | 19.5 |
| 5 | 0.11 | 0.82 | 2.5 | 26 |

# Chapter 4 Project (continued)

**Activity 3: Researching**
Research a hazardous waste clean-up that includes bioremediation. How large is the site? What treatment methods other than bioremediation are being used, if any? Write a few paragraphs summarizing your research. Include data from the site, if possible.

## *Finishing the Project*

The activities should help you complete your project. You should prepare a presentation for the class describing some aspect of a bioremediation project. Your presentation could be a graph or chart analyzing bioremediation data or a poster advertising a bioremediation project.

**Reflect and Revise**
Ask a classmate to review your project with you. After you have seen each other's presentations, decide if your work is complete, clear, and convincing. Make sure that you have included all supporting material from your work on the project. Check that the information you have presented is accurate. You may want to make some changes based on your classmate's review.

**Extending the Project**
Bioremediation is a fairly new field. You can do more research into the field by contacting the United States Department of the Interior. You can also get more information on the Internet.

**Take it to the NET**

Visit PHSchool.com for information and links you might find helpful as you complete your project.

# Chapter Project Manager

• • • • • • • • • • • • • • • • • • • • • • • • • • • • • • • • • • • • • • • • • • • • • • • • • • • • • • • • • • • •

*Chapter 4: Munching Microbes*

**Getting Started**

Read the project. As you work on the project, you will need a calculator and materials on which you can record your calculations and make neat matrices. Keep all of your work for the project in a folder.

| **Checklist** | **Suggestions** |
|---|---|
| ❏ Activity 1: organizing data with matrices | ❏ Arrange amounts of each component in a $5 \times 1$ matrix. |
| ❏ Activity 2: using matrix operations | ❏ Add corresponding entries to find the totals. |
| ❏ Activity 3: researching bioremediation | ❏ Check the Internet for information. |
| ❏ bioremediation report | ❏ How has hazardous waste clean-up changed in the last twenty years? What standards exist by which it is determined that a site is considered hazardous or that a site has been sufficiently cleaned up? Do these standards vary by state? |

**Scoring Rubric**

**3**   Calculations are correct. Matrices are neat and accurate. Explanations are thorough and well thought out. The presentation is accurate and thoroughly explains the information.

**2**   Calculations are mostly correct, with some minor errors. Matrices are neat and mostly accurate with minor errors. The explanations lack detail. The presentation has minor errors or lacks important information.

**1**   Calculations contain both minor and major errors. Matrices are not accurate. The explanations and presentation are inaccurate or incomplete.

**0**   Major elements of the project are incomplete or missing.

**Your Evaluation of Project**   Evaluate your work, based on the *Scoring Rubric*.

**Teacher's Evaluation of Project**

# Chapter Project Teacher Notes

*Chapter 4: Munching Microbes*

**About the Project**
The Chapter Project gives students an opportunity to use matrices to organize data from a bioremediation project. They use the matrices to calculate totals and changes in the amount of wastes present. Then, they research other bioremediation projects and summarize and display their findings.

**Introducing the Project**
Encourage students to keep all project-related materials in a separate folder.

- Ask students if they have been near sites that were being cleaned up after oil or chemical spills. Explain that the field of bioremediation uses naturally-occurring bacteria to degrade hazardous wastes.

- Have students make a list of materials they need to begin the project.

**Activity 1: Organizing**
Students write matrices with data from soil tests for hazardous wastes.

**Activity 2: Calculating**
Students use their previously-written matrices to calculate the total amounts of the hazardous waste components and to show by how much the amount of each component has decreased over 12 months.

**Activity 3: Researching**
Students research a hazardous waste clean-up that includes bioremediation. They then write a report on the clean-up.

**Finishing the Project**
You may wish to plan a project day on which students share their completed projects. Encourage students to explain their processes as well as their results. Ask students to review their project work and update their folders.

- Have students review their methods for organizing the data in matrices, calculating totals and changes in the component amounts, and for researching bioremediation for the project.

- Ask groups to share their insights that resulted from completing the project, such as any shortcuts they found for organizing the data or conducting research.

**Take it to the NET**

Visit PHSchool.com for information, student links, and teacher support for this project.

# ✔ Checkpoint Quiz 1

•••••••••••••••••••••••••••••••••••••••••••••••••••••••••••••••••

*Use with Lessons 4-1 through 4-3.*

**State the dimensions of each matrix. Identify the indicated element.**

**1.** $\begin{bmatrix} 3 & 2 \\ 4 & 1 \end{bmatrix}; a_{21}$
　　　　**2.** $[2 \ \ 6 \ \ 3]; a_{12}$
　　　　**3.** $\begin{bmatrix} 3 & 5 & 9 \\ -1 & 2 & -4 \\ 0 & 6 & 0 \end{bmatrix}; a_{33}$

**Use matrices *E*, *F*, *G*, and *H* below. Perform each operation.**

$$E = \begin{bmatrix} 7 & 0 \\ 3 & -1 \\ -3 & 4 \end{bmatrix} \qquad F = \begin{bmatrix} 5 & -1 \\ 7 & 6 \\ -2 & 0 \end{bmatrix} \qquad G = \begin{bmatrix} 4 & -2 \\ 3 & 1 \end{bmatrix} \qquad H = \begin{bmatrix} -1 & 4 \\ 6 & 2 \end{bmatrix}$$

**4.** $E + F$　　　**5.** $-5G$　　　**6.** $3F$　　　**7.** $2(E + F)$　　　**8.** $GH$　　　**9.** $F - E$

**10. Standardized Test Prep** For which pair of matrices is $\begin{bmatrix} 3 & 4 \\ -9 & -12 \\ 15 & 20 \end{bmatrix}$ the product?

**A.** $[3 \ \ 4]\begin{bmatrix} 1 \\ -3 \\ 5 \end{bmatrix}$　　　**B.** $\begin{bmatrix} 3 & -2 \\ -1 & 4 \end{bmatrix}[3 \ \ 4]$　　　**C.** $\begin{bmatrix} 1 \\ -3 \\ 5 \end{bmatrix}[3 \ \ 4]$　　　**D.** $\begin{bmatrix} 4 \\ 6 \end{bmatrix}\begin{bmatrix} 1 \\ -3 \\ 5 \end{bmatrix}$

- - - - - ✂ - - - - - - - - - - - - - - - - - - - - - - - - - - - - - - - - - - - - -

# ✔ Checkpoint Quiz 2

•••••••••••••••••••••••••••••••••••••••••••••••••••••••••••••••••

*Use with Lessons 4-4 through 4-6.*

**Use △*ABC* with coordinates *A*(1, –3), *B*(2, 1), and *C*(–3, –2). Use a matrix to find the coordinates of the vertices of the image under each transformation.**

**1.** a translation 4 units right and 2 units down
　　　　**2.** a dilation of 4

**3.** a reflection in the *x*-axis
　　　　**4.** a rotation of 270°

**Find the inverse of each matrix, if it exists.**

**5.** $\begin{bmatrix} -2 & -1 \\ 10 & 7 \end{bmatrix}$
　　　　**6.** $\begin{bmatrix} -4 & 2 \\ -5 & 1 \end{bmatrix}$
　　　　**7.** $\begin{bmatrix} 9 & -3 \\ -6 & 2 \end{bmatrix}$

**Solve each matrix equation.**

**8.** $\begin{bmatrix} 3 & 4 \\ 2 & 3 \end{bmatrix}X = \begin{bmatrix} 6 \\ 5 \end{bmatrix}$
　　**9.** $\begin{bmatrix} 2 & -3 \\ 1 & 2 \end{bmatrix}X + \begin{bmatrix} -1 & 7 \\ -2 & 4 \end{bmatrix} = \begin{bmatrix} 9 & 12 \\ 3 & 10 \end{bmatrix}$
　　**10.** $\begin{bmatrix} 1 & -6 & 0 \\ 0 & 1 & -7 \\ 3 & 0 & 2 \end{bmatrix}X = \begin{bmatrix} 1 \\ 4 \\ 11 \end{bmatrix}$

# Chapter Test

# Form A

*Chapter 4*

1. The table shows record high and low temperatures in degrees Fahrenheit in each of six cities.

| City | Record High | Record Low |
|------|-------------|------------|
| **Anchorage** | 85 | −34 |
| **Chicago** | 104 | −27 |
| **Houston** | 107 | 7 |
| **Miami** | 98 | 30 |
| **Pittsburgh** | 103 | −18 |
| **San Diego** | 111 | 29 |

Source: *World Almanac and Book of Facts 1995*

  **a.** Display the data in a matrix whose rows indicate the data for each city. State the dimensions of the matrix.

  **b.** Identify $a_{42}$.

**Find each sum or difference.**

2. $\begin{bmatrix} 9 & 2 \\ 8 & -1 \end{bmatrix} - \begin{bmatrix} 7 & -5 \\ 6 & 3 \end{bmatrix}$

3. $\begin{bmatrix} 1 & 13 & 16 \\ 24 & -3 & 19 \\ 9 & 10 & 20 \end{bmatrix} + \begin{bmatrix} 22 & 7 & -18 \\ 5 & 15 & 11 \\ 12 & 14 & -17 \end{bmatrix}$

**Find each product if possible. If not possible, write *product undefined*.**

4. $\begin{bmatrix} 2 & 1 \\ 3 & 0 \\ 7 & 4 \end{bmatrix}\begin{bmatrix} 2 & 4 \\ 1 & 6 \end{bmatrix}$

5. $-3\begin{bmatrix} 3 & 10 \\ 21 & -4 \end{bmatrix}$

6. $\begin{bmatrix} 9 & 15 & 6 \\ -8 & 2 & 7 \\ 63 & -8 & 1 \end{bmatrix}\begin{bmatrix} 2 & 4 & 0 \\ -5 & 0 & 8 \end{bmatrix}$

7. $\begin{bmatrix} 3 & 2 \\ 0 & 0 \end{bmatrix}\begin{bmatrix} 0 & 1 \\ 4 & 0 \end{bmatrix}$

8. $\triangle ABC$ has coordinates $(1, 1), (3, 4),$ and $(0, -5)$. Write the vertices in matrix form.

  **a.** Find the coordinates of the image of the triangle after a dilation of size $\frac{1}{2}$.

  **b.** Find the coordinates of the image of the triangle after a translation right 3 units and up 2 units.

  **c.** Find the coordinates of the image of the triangle after a rotation of 180°.

  **d.** Find the coordinates of the image of the triangle after a reflection in the line $y = x$.

**Find the determinant of each matrix.**

9. $\begin{bmatrix} -6 & -7 \\ 5 & 8 \end{bmatrix}$

10. $\begin{bmatrix} 1 & -5 \\ -2 & 9 \end{bmatrix}$

11. $\begin{bmatrix} 1 & 2 & 3 \\ 6 & 0 & 5 \\ 0 & 4 & 0 \end{bmatrix}$

# Chapter Test (continued)                    Form A

*Chapter 4*

**Find the inverse of each matrix if it exists. If it does not exist, write**
*no inverse.*

**12.** $\begin{bmatrix} 6 & 2 \\ 3 & 2 \end{bmatrix}$

**13.** $\begin{bmatrix} 7 & 8 \\ -14 & -16 \end{bmatrix}$

**14.** $\begin{bmatrix} 1 & 2 & 3 \\ 2 & 2 & 1 \\ 1 & 1 & 1 \end{bmatrix}$

**15.** $\begin{bmatrix} 4 & 4 & 8 \\ 3 & 2 & 6 \\ 2 & 1 & 4 \end{bmatrix}$

**Solve each matrix equation.**

**16.** $\begin{bmatrix} 3 & 4 \\ -1 & -1 \end{bmatrix} X = \begin{bmatrix} 3 \\ 2 \end{bmatrix}$

**17.** $\begin{bmatrix} 6 & 2 \\ -1 & 4 \end{bmatrix} - X = \begin{bmatrix} 8 & 1 \\ 1 & 3 \end{bmatrix}$

**18.** $X + \begin{bmatrix} 1 & 3 & 6 \\ -1 & 2 & 1 \end{bmatrix} = \begin{bmatrix} 8 & 1 & 0 \\ 14 & 3 & -1 \end{bmatrix}$

**19.** $\begin{bmatrix} -3 & -2 \\ 1 & 1 \end{bmatrix} X = \begin{bmatrix} 8 & -1 \\ 6 & 0 \end{bmatrix}$

**20.** $4X + 3 \begin{bmatrix} 3 & 2 \\ 1 & -2 \end{bmatrix} = \begin{bmatrix} 10 & 8 \\ 5 & -2 \end{bmatrix}$

**21.** $2X = \frac{1}{4} \begin{bmatrix} -6 & 2 \\ 8 & -8 \end{bmatrix}$

**Solve the following systems using inverse matrices. Show your work.**

**22.** $\begin{cases} 2x - y = 2 \\ 2x - 2y = 4 \end{cases}$

**23.** $\begin{cases} 2x + 3y + 4z = 3 \\ -13x + 5y - 2z = 3 \\ -3x + 4y + 3z = 6 \end{cases}$

**24.** Solve $\begin{cases} -3x + 5y = -4 \\ x - 3y = 4 \end{cases}$ using Cramer's Rule. Show your work.

**25.** Solve the system using an augmented matrix. Show your work.
$$\begin{cases} 5x + 4y - z = 1 \\ 2x - 2y + z = 1 \\ -x - y + z = 2 \end{cases}$$

**26.** Write two $2 \times 2$ matrices $A$ and $B$. Show that multiplication of matrices is not commutative.

**27.** Are these matrices inverses of each other? Show why or why not.
$$\begin{bmatrix} 2 & -1 \\ -3 & 1 \end{bmatrix} \quad \text{and} \quad \begin{bmatrix} -1 & -1 \\ -3 & -2 \end{bmatrix}$$

**28.** What are the dimensions of the product of a $2 \times 3$ matrix and a $3 \times 4$ matrix?

**29.** You bought ten carnations and five daisies for a total of $12.50. Later that day you bought five carnations and eight daisies for a total of $11.75. Find the price of each carnation and of each daisy.

# Chapter Test

# Form B

**Chapter 4**

1. The table shows record low and high temperatures in degrees Fahrenheit in each of six states.

| State | Record Low | Record High |
|-------|-----------|-------------|
| **Alaska** | −80 | 100 |
| **California** | −45 | 134 |
| **Florida** | −2 | 109 |
| **Michigan** | −51 | 112 |
| **New Mexico** | −50 | 116 |
| **South Dakota** | −58 | 120 |

Source: *World Almanac and Book of Facts 1995*

   **a.** Display the data in a matrix whose rows indicate the data for each state. State the dimensions of the matrix.

   **b.** Identify $a_{21}$.

**Find each sum or difference.**

2. $\begin{bmatrix} 16 & -2 \\ 1 & 12 \end{bmatrix} - \begin{bmatrix} 14 & 3 \\ 4 & -18 \end{bmatrix}$

3. $\begin{bmatrix} 10 & -1 & 6 \\ 18 & 14 & -5 \\ 2 & 7 & 3 \end{bmatrix} + \begin{bmatrix} 6 & 8 & 20 \\ 2 & 4 & -12 \\ 16 & 8 & -4 \end{bmatrix}$

**Find each product if possible. If not possible, write *product undefined*.**

4. $\begin{bmatrix} 0 & 3 \\ 4 & 6 \\ 5 & 6 \end{bmatrix}\begin{bmatrix} 2 & 5 \\ 1 & 1 \end{bmatrix}$

5. $-5\begin{bmatrix} -8 & 16 \\ 2 & 1 \end{bmatrix}$

6. $\begin{bmatrix} 4 & 12 & 6 \\ -8 & 21 & 0 \\ 6 & -8 & 10 \end{bmatrix}\begin{bmatrix} 21 & 6 & 0 \\ -1 & 0 & -8 \end{bmatrix}$

7. $\begin{bmatrix} 3 & 1 \\ 0 & 2 \end{bmatrix}\begin{bmatrix} 0 & 1 \\ 2 & 0 \end{bmatrix}$

8. A rectangle has coordinates $A(3, 1)$, $B(3, -8)$, $C(-4, 1)$, and $D(-4, -8)$. Write the coordinates of the vertices as a matrix.

   **a.** Find the coordinates of the image of the rectangle after a dilation of size $\frac{1}{4}$.

   **b.** Find the coordinates of the image of the rectangle after a translation left 4 units and down 2 units.

   **c.** Find the coordinates of the image of the rectangle after a rotation of 90°.

   **d.** Find the coordinates of the image of the rectangle after a reflection in line $y = -x$.

**Find the determinant of each matrix.**

9. $\begin{bmatrix} 4 & 2 \\ -9 & -5 \end{bmatrix}$

10. $\begin{bmatrix} -6 & -5 \\ -8 & 7 \end{bmatrix}$

11. $\begin{bmatrix} 0 & 5 & 3 \\ -4 & 7 & 1 \\ -1 & 0 & 2 \end{bmatrix}$

# Chapter Test (continued)          Form B

*Chapter 4*

**Find the inverse of each matrix if it exists. If it does not exist, write**
*no inverse.*

**12.** $\begin{bmatrix} 4 & 5 \\ 8 & 12 \end{bmatrix}$

**13.** $\begin{bmatrix} -3 & 17 \\ -6 & 34 \end{bmatrix}$

**14.** $\begin{bmatrix} 4 & 4 & 3 \\ 6 & 2 & 1 \\ 2 & 1 & 1 \end{bmatrix}$

**15.** $\begin{bmatrix} 3 & 6 & 9 \\ 3 & 7 & 6 \\ -1 & -2 & -3 \end{bmatrix}$

**Solve each matrix equation.**

**16.** $\begin{bmatrix} -3 & -2 \\ 1 & 1 \end{bmatrix} X = \begin{bmatrix} 7 \\ 8 \end{bmatrix}$

**17.** $\begin{bmatrix} 2 & -1 \\ 17 & 8 \end{bmatrix} - X = \begin{bmatrix} 3 & 4 \\ 1 & -1 \end{bmatrix}$

**18.** $X + \begin{bmatrix} 6 & 2 & 0 \\ 1 & 0 & -1 \end{bmatrix} = \begin{bmatrix} 0 & 17 & 8 \\ 3 & -1 & 2 \end{bmatrix}$

**19.** $\begin{bmatrix} 3 & 4 \\ -1 & -1 \end{bmatrix} X = \begin{bmatrix} 6 & 3 \\ 0 & -1 \end{bmatrix}$

**20.** $2X - 3 \begin{bmatrix} 1 & -3 \\ 4 & -5 \end{bmatrix} = \begin{bmatrix} 1 & 5 \\ -4 & -7 \end{bmatrix}$

**21.** $5X = \dfrac{1}{2} \begin{bmatrix} 90 & 20 \\ -70 & -30 \end{bmatrix}$

**Solve the following systems using inverse matrices. Show your work.**

**22.** $\begin{cases} 2x + 4y = 10 \\ x - 3y = -5 \end{cases}$

**23.** $\begin{cases} 3x + 8y - z = -18 \\ 2x + y + 5z = 8 \\ -y + z = 4 \end{cases}$

**24.** Solve $\begin{cases} 2x - 3y = -12 \\ 2x + 7y = 8 \end{cases}$ using Cramer's Rule. Show your work.

**25.** Solve the system using an augmented matrix. Show your work.
$$\begin{cases} x + 2y + z = 1 \\ 2x + 3y + 2z = 0 \\ -x - 3y + 3z = 1 \end{cases}$$

**26.** Use the matrices $A$ and $B$ to find $AB$ and $BA$. Is multiplication of matrices commutative?

$$A = \begin{bmatrix} 0 & 2 \\ 1 & -3 \end{bmatrix} \quad \text{and} \quad B = \begin{bmatrix} -2 & 1 \\ -4 & 5 \end{bmatrix}$$

**27.** If two matrices are inverses of each other, what is their product?

**28.** What are the dimensions of the product of a $20 \times 30$ matrix and a $30 \times 50$ matrix?

**29.** Last year Zach received $469.75 interest from two investments. The interest rates were 7.5% on one account and 8% on the other. The total amount invested was $6000. How much was invested at each rate?

# Alternative Assessment

## Form C

*Chapter 4*

**Give complete answers.**

### TASK 1

**a.** Write a $3 \times 3$ matrix $A$. Discuss the properties that need to exist so that matrices can be added, subtracted, and multiplied.

**b.** Add your matrix to $\begin{bmatrix} 1 & 2 & 3 \\ 4 & 5 & 6 \\ 7 & 8 & 9 \end{bmatrix}$.

**c.** Subtract $\begin{bmatrix} 9 & 8 & 7 \\ 6 & 5 & 4 \\ 3 & 2 & 1 \end{bmatrix}$ from your original matrix.

**d.** Multiply your matrix by $\begin{bmatrix} 1 \\ 2 \\ 3 \end{bmatrix}$. What are the dimensions of the product matrix?

**e.** Find $C$ such that $C - \begin{bmatrix} 3 & 1 & 2 \\ 6 & 4 & 5 \\ 4 & 2 & 1 \end{bmatrix} = A$, your original matrix.

**f.** Write a $2 \times 2$ matrix. Find the inverse of this matrix. If no inverse exists, explain why.

### TASK 2

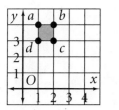

**a.** Organize the $x$- and $y$-coordinates of the vertices of the shaded square into a $2 \times 4$ matrix.

**b.** What matrix will translate the square 2 units left and 1 unit down?

**c.** What matrix operation is necessary to perform this translation?

**d.** What are the vertices of the new square?

**e.** Find the coordinates of the image of the original square after a dilation of 2.

# Alternative Assessment (continued)    Form C

*Chapter 4*

## TASK 3

**a.** Find $A^{-1}$ if $A = \begin{bmatrix} 2 & a^2 \\ \frac{1}{a} & a \end{bmatrix}$. Assume $a \neq 0$.

**b.** Find $A^{-1}A$ and $AA^{-1}$. Are the products $A^{-1}A$ and $AA^{-1}$ always the same matrix? Explain.

**c.** In general, for $2 \times 2$ matrices $A$ and $B$, does $AB$ equal $BA$? Explain.

## TASK 4

Solve each system using inverse matrices. Show all steps in your solution.

**a.** $\begin{cases} 8x - 2y = 14 \\ 12x + 3y = 9 \end{cases}$

**b.** $\begin{cases} 5x + 4y = -9 \\ -6x - 5y = 10.5 \end{cases}$

**c.** $\begin{cases} x + 2y - 2z = 5 \\ x - y + 2z = -10 \\ -x + z = 15 \end{cases}$

**d.** $\begin{cases} -2x + 4y - z = -6 \\ x - z = 1 \\ -x + y = -5 \end{cases}$

# Cumulative Review

· · · · · · · · · · · · · · · · · · · · · · · · · · · · · · · · · · · · · · · · · · · · · · · · · · · · · · · · · · ·

*Chapters 1–4*

**For Exercises 1–14, choose the correct letter.**

1. Which line is perpendicular to $y = \frac{3}{4}x - 1$?

   **A.** $y = \frac{4}{3}x - 5$     **B.** $y = -\frac{3}{4}x + 2$     **C.** $y = -\frac{4}{3}x + 6$     **D.** $y = \frac{3}{4}x - 3$

2. Which number is an integer?

   **A.** $\sqrt{6}$     **B.** $\frac{3}{5}$     **C.** $-3$     **D.** $0.74$

3. Which ordered pair is a solution of the system $\begin{cases} x - y \geq 2 \\ x + y \leq 7 \end{cases}$?

   **A.** $(5, 1)$     **B.** $(-2, 4)$     **C.** $(6, 5)$     **D.** $(-1, -2)$

4. Find $\begin{bmatrix} 3 & 2 \\ 1 & 3 \end{bmatrix}\begin{bmatrix} 2 & 1 \\ 4 & 1 \end{bmatrix}$.

   **A.** $\begin{bmatrix} 14 & 5 \\ 14 & 4 \end{bmatrix}$     **B.** $\begin{bmatrix} 3 & 2 & 2 & 1 \\ 1 & 3 & 4 & 1 \end{bmatrix}$     **C.** $\begin{bmatrix} 14 & 3 \\ 14 & 3 \end{bmatrix}$     **D.** $\begin{bmatrix} 14 & 5 \\ 9 & 4 \end{bmatrix}$

5. What is the equation of a line with slope 3 passing through $(1, 0)$?

   **A.** $y = 3x + 3$     **B.** $y = 3x$     **C.** $y = 3x - 3$     **D.** $y = 3(x - 3)$

6. Which point lies on the graph of $7x - 5y + 2z = 70$?

   **A.** $(10, -1, 2)$     **B.** $(2, -10, 3)$     **C.** $(0, 5, 10)$     **D.** $(2, -7, 20)$

7. Find the value of 6!.

   **A.** 21     **B.** 30     **C.** 360     **D.** 720

8. Which line contains the point $(2, 3)$?

   **A.** $y = x - 1$     **B.** $y = x + 1$     **C.** $y + 1 = x$     **D.** $3y = 2x$

9. For which matrix is $a_{21} = 5$?

   **A.** $\begin{bmatrix} 5 & 1 \\ 2 & 3 \end{bmatrix}$     **B.** $\begin{bmatrix} 1 & 5 \\ 3 & 2 \end{bmatrix}$     **C.** $\begin{bmatrix} 2 & 3 \\ 1 & 5 \end{bmatrix}$     **D.** $\begin{bmatrix} 3 & 1 \\ 5 & 2 \end{bmatrix}$

10. Solve $\begin{bmatrix} 1 & 2 \\ 3 & -4 \end{bmatrix}X = \begin{bmatrix} 3 \\ 4 \end{bmatrix}$.

    **A.** $\begin{bmatrix} 11 \\ -7 \end{bmatrix}$     **B.** $\begin{bmatrix} 2 & \frac{1}{2} \end{bmatrix}$     **C.** $[11 \quad -7]$     **D.** $\begin{bmatrix} 2 \\ \frac{1}{2} \end{bmatrix}$

11. At which vertex is the objective function $C = -3x + 7y$ maximized?

    **A.** $(0, 1)$     **B.** $(5, 2)$     **C.** $(-3, 6)$     **D.** $(-1, -4)$

# Cumulative Review (continued)

*Chapters 1–4*

**12.** Find $\begin{bmatrix} 5 & 9 \\ 44 & 21 \end{bmatrix} - \begin{bmatrix} 2 & 1 \\ 4 & 0 \end{bmatrix}$.

**A.** $\begin{bmatrix} 7 & 10 \\ 48 & 21 \end{bmatrix}$　　**B.** $\begin{bmatrix} 3 & 8 \\ 44 & 0 \end{bmatrix}$　　**C.** $\begin{bmatrix} 3 & 8 \\ 44 & 0 \end{bmatrix}$　　**D.** $\begin{bmatrix} 3 & 8 \\ 40 & 21 \end{bmatrix}$

**13.** The coordinates of the vertices of a triangle are $(3, -2), (2, 5)$, and $(-4, 0)$. Give the coordinates of the vertices of the reflection of the triangle in the line $y = x$. Hint: The matrix for a reflection in the line $y = x$ is $\begin{bmatrix} 0 & 1 \\ 1 & 0 \end{bmatrix}$.

**A.** $(3, -2), (2, 5), (-4, 0)$　　　　**B.** $(-3, 2), (-2, -5), (4, 0)$

**C.** $(-2, 3), (5, 2), (0, -4)$　　　　**D.** $(2, -3), (-5, -2), (0, 4)$

**14.** Which matrix is the inverse of $\begin{bmatrix} 1 & 1 & 1 \\ 1 & 0 & 1 \\ 0 & 0 & 1 \end{bmatrix}$?

**A.** $\begin{bmatrix} 1 & 1 & 0 \\ 1 & 0 & 1 \\ 1 & 0 & 1 \end{bmatrix}$　　**B.** $\begin{bmatrix} 1 & 1 & 1 \\ 1 & 0 & 1 \\ 1 & 0 & 0 \end{bmatrix}$　　**C.** $\begin{bmatrix} 0 & 1 & 1 \\ 1 & 1 & 0 \\ 0 & 0 & 1 \end{bmatrix}$　　**D.** $\begin{bmatrix} 0 & 1 & -1 \\ 1 & -1 & 0 \\ 0 & 0 & 1 \end{bmatrix}$

**Compare the quantity in Column A with that in Column B. Choose the best answer.**

**A.** The quantity in Column A is greater.

**B.** The quantity in Column B is greater.

**C.** The two quantities are equal.

**D.** The relationship cannot be determined on the basis of the information supplied.

| Column A | Column B |
|---|---|
| **15.** the $x$-intercept of $3x = 4y$ | the $x$-intercept of $5x = 6y$ |
| **16.** determinant of $\begin{bmatrix} 2 & 8 \\ 4 & 2 \end{bmatrix}$ | determinant of $\begin{bmatrix} 1 & 8 \\ 0 & 12 \end{bmatrix}$ |

**17. Open-Ended** Write the coordinates of the vertices of a geometric figure and its image after a dilation of $\frac{1}{2}$. Graph the preimage and image.

**18. Writing** Describe the process of solving the system $\begin{cases} 2x - 3y = 5 \\ x - 2y = 4 \end{cases}$ by using the elimination method.

# Chapter 4 Answers

## Practice 4-1

**1.** $3 \times 1; -3$  **2.** $3 \times 4; 5$  **3.** $2 \times 3; 12$  **4.** $3 \times 3; q$
**5.** $3 \times 2; 4$  **6.** $1 \times 4; -4$

**7.** $\begin{bmatrix} 17.6 & 8.3 & 5.4 & 8.7 & 4.0 & 6.6 & 3.5 \\ 9.5 & 5.1 & 4.5 & 6.4 & 2.6 & 5.1 & 2.7 \end{bmatrix}$

**8.** $2 \times 7$  **9.** 9.5; percent unemployment in construction in June, 1996  **10.** 6.6; percent unemployment in services in June, 1992  **11.** Answers may vary.

Sample: $M = \begin{bmatrix} 3900 & 3300 \\ 400 & 150 \\ 100 & 50 \end{bmatrix}$  **12.** $3 \times 2$

**13.** number of days lost to strikes per 1,000 employees in Greece in the given years  **14.** number of days lost to strikes per 1,000 employees in the United States from 1990 to 1994

## Practice 4-2

**1.** $a = 5; b = -\frac{7}{2}; c = 12; d = 7$  **2.** $c = \frac{5}{3}; y = -7;$
$x = 4; z = \frac{7}{2}; a = -3; b = 0$  **3.** $x = 3; z = -2$

**4.** $M = \begin{bmatrix} 37 & 56 \\ 0 & 76 \\ 87 & 102 \\ 6 & 27 \end{bmatrix}; F = \begin{bmatrix} 23 & 58 \\ 93 & 82 \\ 0 & 34 \\ 18 & 29 \end{bmatrix}$

**5.** $M - F = \begin{bmatrix} 14 & -2 \\ -93 & -6 \\ 87 & 68 \\ -12 & -2 \end{bmatrix}$  **6.** $\begin{bmatrix} -2 & 3 \\ 2 & 0 \end{bmatrix}$

**7.** $\begin{bmatrix} 8 & -5 & -6 \\ 3 & -8 & 12 \\ 4 & -12 & -18 \end{bmatrix}$  **8.** $\begin{bmatrix} -2 & 2 \\ -6 & 5 \\ -4 & -2 \end{bmatrix}$  **9.** $\begin{bmatrix} -7 \\ -4 \\ 23 \end{bmatrix}$

**10.** $\begin{bmatrix} 8 & 11 \\ 13 & 14 \\ 4 & 11 \end{bmatrix}$  **11.** $\begin{bmatrix} -27 & 101 & -2 \\ -19 & 93 & -1 \\ -8 & -1 & 20 \end{bmatrix}$  **12.** $\begin{bmatrix} -1 & -4 \\ 0 & 4 \end{bmatrix}$

**13.** $\begin{bmatrix} 0 & -4 & 3 \\ -4 & -2 & 5 \end{bmatrix}$  **14.** not equal; dimensions are different

**15.** equal; dimensions and corresponding elements are equal

## Practice 4-3

**1.** product undefined  **2.** $\begin{bmatrix} 6 & -2 \\ 6 & 0 \end{bmatrix}$  **3.** $\begin{bmatrix} 4 & 1 \\ -3 & 7 \end{bmatrix}$

**4.** difference undefined  **5.** $\begin{bmatrix} 4 & -1 \\ 3 & 1 \end{bmatrix}$  **6.** $\begin{bmatrix} 1 & -1 \\ 3 & -2 \end{bmatrix}$

**7.** product undefined  **8.** $\begin{bmatrix} 0 & 2 \\ -2 & 1 \\ -1 & 0 \end{bmatrix}$  **9.** product undefined

**10.** $\begin{bmatrix} 16 \\ 20 \end{bmatrix}$  **11.** $\begin{bmatrix} 3 & -3 & -1 \\ 2 & -2 & 4 \end{bmatrix}$

**12.** product undefined  **13.** $\begin{bmatrix} 7 & 3 \\ 0 & 2 \end{bmatrix}$  **14.** $\begin{bmatrix} 2 & 0 \\ 0 & 2 \end{bmatrix}$

**15.** product undefined  **16.** $\begin{bmatrix} 0 & 0.4 \\ -0.4 & 0.2 \\ -0.2 & 0 \end{bmatrix}$

**17.** $\begin{bmatrix} \frac{3}{4} & -\frac{3}{4} & -\frac{1}{4} \\ \frac{1}{2} & -\frac{1}{2} & 1 \end{bmatrix}$  **18.** $\begin{bmatrix} 0.5 & -0.5 & -2.5 \\ 2.5 & -2.5 & -5.5 \end{bmatrix}$

**19.** product undefined  **20.** product undefined

**21.** $3 \times 4; \begin{bmatrix} 1 & 2 & 3 & 4 \\ 2 & 4 & 6 & 8 \\ 3 & 6 & 9 & 12 \end{bmatrix}$  **22.** $2 \times 2; \begin{bmatrix} 71 & 34 \\ 49 & 56 \end{bmatrix}$

**23.** $2 \times 2; \begin{bmatrix} 4 & 5 \\ 5 & 4 \end{bmatrix}$  **24.** $\begin{bmatrix} 72 & 24 \\ 60 & 72 \\ 0 & -12 \end{bmatrix}$

**25.** $\begin{bmatrix} -13 & 19 & -8 \\ -24 & 42 & -14 \\ -5 & 8 & -3 \end{bmatrix}$  **26.** $\begin{bmatrix} -1 & 1 & 1 \\ -6 & 5 & 5 \end{bmatrix}$  **27.** $\begin{bmatrix} 11 & 10 \\ 11 & 10 \\ 11 & 10 \end{bmatrix}$

**28.** $\begin{bmatrix} 8 & 14 & 14 & 12 \\ 16 & 8 & 8 & 10 \\ 18 & 18 & 20 & 14 \end{bmatrix}$  **29.** $\begin{bmatrix} 51 & 24 \\ 117 & 55 \end{bmatrix}$  **30.** $\begin{bmatrix} -3 & \frac{8}{3} \\ \frac{5}{3} & -2 \end{bmatrix}$

**31.** $\begin{bmatrix} 2 & 2 \\ 4 & \frac{20}{3} \end{bmatrix}$

## Practice 4-4

**1.** $\begin{bmatrix} 44 & 44 & -33 \\ 22 & -22 & 0 \end{bmatrix}$  **2.** $\begin{bmatrix} 5 & 5 & -2 \\ 6 & 2 & 4 \end{bmatrix}$

**3.** $\begin{bmatrix} 6 & 6 & -4.5 \\ 3 & -3 & 0 \end{bmatrix}$  **4.** $\begin{bmatrix} 6 & 6 & -1 \\ -4 & -8 & -6 \end{bmatrix}$

**5.** $\begin{bmatrix} 2 & -2 & 0 \\ 4 & 4 & -3 \end{bmatrix}$  **6.** $\begin{bmatrix} 2 & -2 & 0 \\ -4 & -4 & 3 \end{bmatrix}$

**7.** $\begin{bmatrix} -2 & 2 & 0 \\ 4 & 4 & -3 \end{bmatrix}$  **8.** $\begin{bmatrix} 3 & 3 & -4 \\ 0 & -4 & -2 \end{bmatrix}$  **9.** $\begin{bmatrix} 1 & 1 & -6 \\ 3 & -1 & 1 \end{bmatrix}$

**10.** $\begin{bmatrix} 2 & 2 & -1.5 \\ 1 & -1 & 0 \end{bmatrix}$  **11.** $\begin{bmatrix} 4 & 4 & -3 \\ -2 & 2 & 0 \end{bmatrix}$

**12.**  **13.**

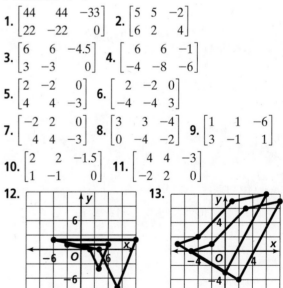

# Chapter 4 Answers (continued)

**14.**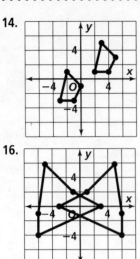

**15.**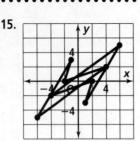

**16.**

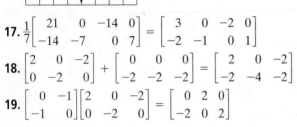

**17.** $\dfrac{1}{7}\begin{bmatrix} 21 & 0 & -14 & 0 \\ -14 & -7 & 0 & 7 \end{bmatrix} = \begin{bmatrix} 3 & 0 & -2 & 0 \\ -2 & -1 & 0 & 1 \end{bmatrix}$

**18.** $\begin{bmatrix} 2 & 0 & -2 \\ 0 & -2 & 0 \end{bmatrix} + \begin{bmatrix} 0 & 0 & 0 \\ -2 & -2 & -2 \end{bmatrix} = \begin{bmatrix} 2 & 0 & -2 \\ -2 & -4 & -2 \end{bmatrix}$

**19.** $\begin{bmatrix} 0 & -1 \\ -1 & 0 \end{bmatrix}\begin{bmatrix} 2 & 0 & -2 \\ 0 & -2 & 0 \end{bmatrix} = \begin{bmatrix} 0 & 2 & 0 \\ -2 & 0 & 2 \end{bmatrix}$

## Practice 4-5

**1.** $\begin{bmatrix} 1 & 1 \\ \frac{1}{2} & 1 \end{bmatrix}$  **2.** $\begin{bmatrix} \frac{1}{2} & \frac{1}{2} \\ -\frac{1}{2} & \frac{1}{2} \end{bmatrix}$  **3.** $\begin{bmatrix} 0 & 1 \\ -1 & 2 \end{bmatrix}$  **4.** $\begin{bmatrix} -1 & 3 \\ 1 & -2 \end{bmatrix}$

**5.** $\begin{bmatrix} -3 & 4 \\ 1 & -1 \end{bmatrix}$  **6.** $\begin{bmatrix} -5 & 7 \\ 3 & -4 \end{bmatrix}$  **7.** $\begin{bmatrix} \frac{1}{6} & -\frac{1}{6} \\ \frac{1}{8} & \frac{1}{8} \end{bmatrix}$

**8.** No inverse; the determinant of the matrix is zero.

**9.** $\begin{bmatrix} -2 & 1 \\ \frac{3}{2} & -\frac{1}{2} \end{bmatrix}$  **10.** $\begin{bmatrix} -\frac{3}{10} & -\frac{2}{5} \\ -\frac{5}{2} & -3 \end{bmatrix}$

**11.** no inverse, cannot be solved  **12.** $\begin{bmatrix} 1 \\ 2 \end{bmatrix}$  **13.** $\begin{bmatrix} 3 \\ 4 \end{bmatrix}$

**14.** $-1$  **15.** $-21$  **16.** $14$  **17.** $-29$  **18.** $9$  **19.** $36$
**20.** yes  **21.** yes  **22.** yes

## Practice 4-6

**1.** $\begin{bmatrix} 3 & 10 & 6 \\ -1 & -5 & -3 \\ -2 & -7 & -4 \end{bmatrix}$  **2.** $\begin{bmatrix} 3 & -1 & -1 \\ -6 & 3 & 2 \\ 4 & -2 & -1 \end{bmatrix}$

**3.** $\begin{bmatrix} -9 & 11 & 19 \\ 1 & -1 & -2 \\ 5 & -6 & -10 \end{bmatrix}$  **4.** no inverse

**5.** $\begin{bmatrix} 0.65 & -1.45 & -0.2 \\ -0.8 & 1.4 & 0.4 \\ 0.4 & -0.2 & -0.2 \end{bmatrix}$  **6.** no inverse

**7.** $\begin{bmatrix} -0.6 & 0 & -0.2 \\ 0 & -0.5 & 0 \\ -0.4 & 0 & 0.2 \end{bmatrix}$  **8.** $\begin{bmatrix} -0.\overline{4} & -0.\overline{4} & -0.\overline{1} \\ 0.\overline{2} & 0.\overline{5} & 0.\overline{2} \\ -0.\overline{1} & 0.\overline{2} & -0.\overline{1} \end{bmatrix}$

**9.** $\begin{bmatrix} 4 \\ -5 \\ 3 \end{bmatrix}$  **10.** $\begin{bmatrix} -3 \\ 1 \\ -2 \end{bmatrix}$  **11.** no inverse, cannot be solved

**12.** $39$  **13.** $-47$  **14.** $-7$  **15.** $9$  **16.** $26$  **17.** $-42$
**18.** no  **19.** yes

## Practice 4-7

**1.** $(0.251, 0.3, 0.07)$  **2.** $(0.7, -0.3, -0.2)$  **3.** $(1, 5, -5)$
**4.** $(2, 1)$  **5.** $(2, 1, -9)$  **6.** $(3, 2)$  **7.** $(-5, 15, 21)$  **8.** $(-1, 0)$
**9.** $(0, 6, 2.8)$  **10.** $(-2, -1)$  **11.** $(-1, 7, -3)$  **12.** $(4, 2, -8)$

| coefficient | variable | constant |
|---|---|---|

**13.** $\begin{bmatrix} 6 & 9 \\ 4 & 13 \end{bmatrix}$  $\begin{bmatrix} x \\ y \end{bmatrix}$  $=$  $\begin{bmatrix} 36 \\ 2 \end{bmatrix}$

**14.** $\begin{bmatrix} 3 & -4 \\ 0 & 7 \end{bmatrix}$  $\begin{bmatrix} x \\ y \end{bmatrix}$  $=$  $\begin{bmatrix} -9 \\ 24 \end{bmatrix}$

**15.** $\begin{bmatrix} 4 & 0 & -1 \\ 12 & 2 & 0 \\ 1 & -1 & 12 \end{bmatrix}$  $\begin{bmatrix} x \\ y \\ z \end{bmatrix}$  $=$  $\begin{bmatrix} 9 \\ 17 \\ 3 \end{bmatrix}$

**16.** $\begin{cases} x + y = 548{,}303 \\ 0.2553415x + 0.1167209y = 110{,}017 \end{cases}$;
$(331{,}975.0482, 216{,}327.9518)$; about $331{,}975$ doctors

**17.** $\begin{cases} x + y = 50 \\ 425x + 550y = 25{,}000 \end{cases}$; $(20, 30)$;
20 one-bedroom and 30 two-bedroom apartments

**18.** $\left(\dfrac{3}{17}, -\dfrac{33}{17}\right)$  **19.** $\left(8, \dfrac{4}{3}\right)$  **20.** no unique solution

**21.** $(4, -32)$  **22.** det $A = 10$, has a unique solution
**23.** det $A = 0$, no unique solution  **24.** det $A = -5$, has a
unique solution

## Practice 4-8

**1.** $\begin{cases} 4x - 2y = 3 \\ 6x + 11y = 9 \end{cases}$  **2.** $\begin{cases} 12x + 6y = -4 \\ -x = 2 \end{cases}$

**3.** $\begin{cases} -2x + 9y - 2z = 20 \\ 3x - y + 2z = 29 \\ 6x + 5y + 5z = -4 \end{cases}$  **4.** $(2, -3)$  **5.** $(6, 2)$

**6.** $(-3, 2)$  **7.** $(0.9, 0.08, 0.3)$  **8.** $(0.25, 0.75, 0.5)$  **9.** $(3, 1, -2)$

**10.** $\left[\begin{array}{cc|c} -3 & 4 & -8 \\ 2 & -8 & 16 \end{array}\right]$  **11.** $\left[\begin{array}{cc|c} 1 & 3 & -30 \\ 4 & 1 & 1 \end{array}\right]$

**12.** $\left[\begin{array}{ccc|c} 1 & -4 & 1 & -9 \\ 3 & 2 & -3 & 9 \\ 4 & 0 & 2 & -4 \end{array}\right]$  **13.** $(-6, -8, 14)$  **14.** $(9, -3, -6)$

**15.** $(7, 1, 0)$  **16.** $(2, 6, -4)$  **17.** $(-1, 7, 0.5)$  **18.** $(-4, 3, 9)$
**19.** $(5, 8, -2)$  **20.** $(1, 7, -9)$  **21.** $(-2, 3, 5)$

*Algebra 2* Chapter 4

# Chapter 4 Answers (continued)

## Reteaching 4-1
**1.** Answers may vary. Check students' work.
**2.** Trial   1   2   3   4
Left $\begin{bmatrix} 36 & 24 & 26 & 55 \\ 15 & 43 & 22 & 46 \end{bmatrix}$
Right
**3.** Check students' work.

## Reteaching 4-2
**1.** $\begin{bmatrix} -2 & 3 \\ 14 & -2 \end{bmatrix}$ **2.** $\begin{bmatrix} -5 & 1 \\ 1 & 2 \end{bmatrix}$ **3.** $\begin{bmatrix} -1 & -1 \\ 1 & -2 \end{bmatrix}$

**4.** $\begin{bmatrix} 1 & 1 & -1 \\ -3 & 1 & -5 \end{bmatrix}$ **5.** $\begin{bmatrix} -16 & -1 & -4 \\ 7 & -7 & -6 \end{bmatrix}$ **6.** $\begin{bmatrix} 4.5 & 5.5 \\ 3 & 11.5 \end{bmatrix}$

**7.** $\begin{bmatrix} -9 & -6 \\ 0 & 1 \\ 8 & 5 \end{bmatrix}$ **8.** $\begin{bmatrix} 5 & 5 \\ 12 & 4 \\ -17 & -2 \end{bmatrix}$ **9.** $\begin{bmatrix} -9 & 7 \\ 3.5 & -6.5 \\ 1.5 & 0 \\ -3.5 & 5 \end{bmatrix}$

**10.** $\begin{bmatrix} -5 & -3 & 8 \\ 3 & -2 & -4 \\ 7 & -5 & 6 \end{bmatrix}$

## Reteaching 4-3

**1.** $\begin{bmatrix} 1 & 3 \\ -6 & 17 \end{bmatrix}$ **2.** $\begin{bmatrix} 0 & 26 \\ -8 & 3 \\ -13 & 33 \\ -7 & 32 \end{bmatrix}$ **3.** $[8 \quad 5 \quad 4]$

## Reteaching 4-4
**1.** $A'B'C'D' = \begin{bmatrix} 1 & -1 & 2 & 4 \\ -2 & 1 & 2 & 0 \end{bmatrix}$

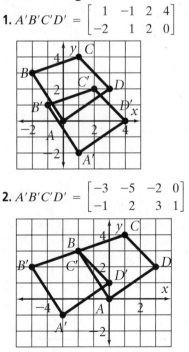

**2.** $A'B'C'D' = \begin{bmatrix} -3 & -5 & -2 & 0 \\ -1 & 2 & 3 & 1 \end{bmatrix}$

**3.** $A'B'C'D' = \begin{bmatrix} -4 & -6 & -3 & -1 \\ 3 & 6 & 7 & 5 \end{bmatrix}$

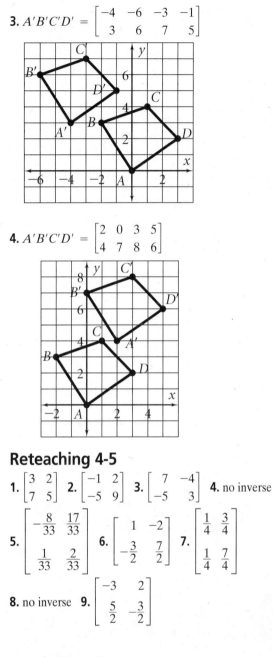

**4.** $A'B'C'D' = \begin{bmatrix} 2 & 0 & 3 & 5 \\ 4 & 7 & 8 & 6 \end{bmatrix}$

## Reteaching 4-5
**1.** $\begin{bmatrix} 3 & 2 \\ 7 & 5 \end{bmatrix}$ **2.** $\begin{bmatrix} -1 & 2 \\ -5 & 9 \end{bmatrix}$ **3.** $\begin{bmatrix} 7 & -4 \\ -5 & 3 \end{bmatrix}$ **4.** no inverse

**5.** $\begin{bmatrix} -\dfrac{8}{33} & \dfrac{17}{33} \\ \dfrac{1}{33} & \dfrac{2}{33} \end{bmatrix}$ **6.** $\begin{bmatrix} 1 & -2 \\ -\dfrac{3}{2} & \dfrac{7}{2} \end{bmatrix}$ **7.** $\begin{bmatrix} \dfrac{1}{4} & \dfrac{3}{4} \\ \dfrac{1}{4} & \dfrac{7}{4} \end{bmatrix}$

**8.** no inverse **9.** $\begin{bmatrix} -3 & 2 \\ \dfrac{5}{2} & -\dfrac{3}{2} \end{bmatrix}$

## Reteaching 4-6
**1.** $-6$ **2.** $-21$ **3.** 14 **4.** $-50$ **5.** 17 **6.** $-3$

## Reteaching 4-7
**1.** $(2,1)$ **2.** $(2,1)$ **3.** $(-1,0)$ **4.** no unique solution

## Reteaching 4-8
**1.** $(-1,-1)$ **2.** $(-1,-2)$ **3.** $(-4,-14)$

## Enrichment 4-1
I think and think for months and years. Ninety-nine times,
the conclusion is false. The hundredth time I am right.
—Albert Einstein

# Chapter 4 Answers (continued)

## Enrichment 4-2
EUCLID OHIO

$$\begin{bmatrix} 3 & 0 \\ 4 & -7 \\ 2 & -8 \end{bmatrix}; \begin{bmatrix} 1 & 5 & 11 \\ -1 & 4 & 6 \\ 0 & 3 & 5 \end{bmatrix}; \begin{bmatrix} -1 & 6 & -2 \\ 0 & 10 & -2 \end{bmatrix};$$

$$\begin{bmatrix} 3 & -6 & 8 & 5 \\ 2 & 4 & 4 & 2 \\ 0 & -3 & 11 & -4 \end{bmatrix}; \begin{bmatrix} -4 & -3 & 0 & 2 \\ 5 & 5 & 2 & -1 \\ 1 & 1 & -6 & -6 \end{bmatrix};$$

$$\begin{bmatrix} -1 & -2 & 0 \\ 1 & -1 & -1 \\ 10 & -2 & -1 \end{bmatrix}; \begin{bmatrix} 4 & -2 & -4 & -3 & 7 \\ 7 & 1 & 0 & -3 & 10 \\ 2 & 3 & -3 & 1 & 1 \end{bmatrix};$$

$$\begin{bmatrix} 4 & 3 & -7 & 4 \\ 3 & -2 & 0 & -2 \\ 4 & 9 & -3 & 6 \end{bmatrix}; \begin{bmatrix} -2 & 1 & 3 \\ -7 & -2 & 2 \\ 5 & 0 & -3 \end{bmatrix};$$

$$\begin{bmatrix} -1 & 5 & 0 & -4 \\ 2 & -5 & -1 & 5 \\ 5 & -4 & 3 & 2 \end{bmatrix}$$

## Enrichment 4-3

**1.** The number of rows must be the same as the number of columns.; so it can be multiplied by itself;

$$\begin{bmatrix} 0 & 0 \\ 0 & 0 \end{bmatrix}; \begin{bmatrix} 0 & 0 \\ 0 & 0 \end{bmatrix};$$ A nonzero matrix may be nilpotent.

**2.** $\begin{bmatrix} a^2 + bc & ab + bd \\ ac + cd & bc + d^2 \end{bmatrix}$

**3.** $a^2 + bc = 0; ab + bd = 0;$
$ac + cd = 0; bc + d^2 = 0$

**4.** $b(a + d) = 0$ **5.** $b = 0; a + d = 0$

**6.** $a^2 = 0,$ so $a = 0; d^2 = 0,$ so $d = 0$

**7.** $A = \begin{bmatrix} 0 & 0 \\ c & 0 \end{bmatrix}; A^2 = \begin{bmatrix} 0 & 0 \\ 0 & 0 \end{bmatrix}$ **8.** $\begin{bmatrix} 0 & b \\ 0 & 0 \end{bmatrix}$

## Enrichment 4-4

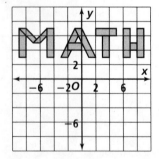

## Enrichment 4-5

**1.** $ad - bc$ **2.** $eh - fg$ **3.** $adeh + bcfg - bceh - adfg$

**4.** $\begin{bmatrix} ae + bg & af + bh \\ ce + dg & cf + dh \end{bmatrix}$

**5.** $(ae + bg)(cf + dh) - (af + bh)(ce + dg)$
$= adeh + bcfg - bceh - adfg$

**6.** $\det(AB) = \det A \cdot \det B$

**7.** The determinant of the product of two matrices is equal to the product of the determinants.

**8.** $\det I; 1; \dfrac{1}{\det A}$ **9.** The determinant of the inverse of a matrix is equal to the reciprocal (inverse) of the determinant of the original matrix.

## Enrichment 4-6

**1.** $\det A = a_1(b_2c_3 - b_3c_2) - b_1(a_2c_3 - a_3c_2)$
$\qquad + c_1(a_2b_3 - a_3b_2)$
$= a_1b_2c_3 - a_1b_3c_2 - a_2b_1c_3 + a_3b_1c_2$
$\qquad + a_2b_3c_1 - a_3b_2c_1$
$= a_1b_2c_3 + a_2b_3c_1 + a_3b_1c_2$
$\qquad - (a_1b_3c_2 + a_2b_1c_3 + a_3b_2c_1)$

**2.** 25 **3.** 0 **4.** Answers may vary. Sample: $\begin{bmatrix} 1 & 2 & 3 \\ 1 & 2 & 3 \\ 4 & 5 & 6 \end{bmatrix}; 0$

**5.** Answers may vary. Sample: $\begin{bmatrix} 1 & 2 \\ 1 & 2 \end{bmatrix}; 0$

**6.** Its determinant is zero.

## Enrichment 4-7

**1.** Let $b$ equal the weight of the bread in the sandwich. Let $m$ equal the weight of the meat in the sandwich. Let $c$ equal the weight of the cheese in the sandwich. The three equations are:
$$\begin{cases} b + m + c = 12 \\ 0.6b + 3m + 1.5c = 1.50(12) \\ 10b + 50m + 40c = 30(12) \end{cases}$$
5 lb bread; 3 lb meat; 4 lb cheese

**2.** Let $c, r,$ and $s$ represent the number of pounds of chicken, rice and shellfish, respectively. The three equations are:
$$\begin{cases} c + r + s = 18 \\ 1c + 0.5r + 3s = 19 \\ 100c + 20r + 50s = 850 \end{cases}$$
10 lb rice; 5 lb chicken; 3 lb shellfish

**3.** Let $y, t,$ and $b$ represent the price per pound of frozen yogurt, topping, and bananas, respectively.
The three equations are:
$$\begin{cases} 2b + 3t + 4y = 19 \\ -t + y = 1 \\ -4b - \frac{1}{2}t + y = 0 \end{cases}$$
frozen yogurt: $3.00/lb; topping: $2.00/lb; bananas: $.50/lb

**4.** Let $b, y,$ and $t$ represent the number of calories per pound in bananas, frozen yogurt, and topping, respectively. The three equations are:
$$\begin{cases} 2b + 3t + 4y = 5400 \\ \frac{1}{2}t - y = 0 \\ 5b - 2t + 2y = 0 \end{cases}$$
frozen yogurt: 500 cal; topping: 1000 cal; bananas: 200 cal

## Enrichment 4-8

**1a.** 2600, 2400

**1b.** $\begin{cases} 1.01x + y = 5000 \\ 3x - 2y = 3000 \end{cases}$; 2589.64, 2384.46

**1c.** $\begin{cases} x + 0.99y = 5000 \\ 3x - 2y = 3000 \end{cases}$; 2609.66, 2414.49

**1d.** $\begin{cases} x + y = 5000 \\ 3.03x - 2y = 3000 \end{cases}$; 2584.49, 2415.51

**1e.** $\begin{cases} x + y = 5000 \\ 3x - 2.02y = 3000 \end{cases}$; 2609.56, 2390.44

**1f.** well-conditioned

**2a.** 1, 5000

**2b.** $\begin{cases} 1.01x + y = 5001 \\ 3x - 2y = -9997 \end{cases}$; 1.00, 4999.99

**2c.** $\begin{cases} x + 0.99y = 5001 \\ 3x - 2y = -9997 \end{cases}$; 21.12, 5030.18

**2d.** $\begin{cases} x + y = 5001 \\ 3.03x - 2y = -9997 \end{cases}$; 0.99, 5000.01

**2e.** $\begin{cases} x + y = 5001 \\ 3x - 2.02y = -9997 \end{cases}$; 20.92, 4980.08

**2f.** ill-conditioned

## Chapter Project

**Activity 1: Organizing**

| | B | | T | | E | | X |
|---|---|---|---|---|---|---|---|
| 1 | 0.06 | 1 | 0.95 | 1 | 0.9 | 1 | 18.5 |
| 2 | 0.06 | 2 | 1.05 | 2 | 0.73 | 2 | 13.5 |
| 3 | 0.35 | 3 | 6 | 3 | 5.6 | 3 | 49 |
| 4 | 0.22 | 4 | 0.19 | 4 | 2 | 4 | 19.5 |
| 5 | 0.11 | 5 | 0.82 | 5 | 2.5 | 5 | 26 |

; Check students' work.

**Activity 2: Calculating**

combined amounts (mg/kg): 20.41, 15.34, 60.95, 21.91, 29.43

| | B | | T | | E | | X |
|---|---|---|---|---|---|---|---|
| 1 | 0.01 | 1 | 0.90 | 1 | 0.85 | 1 | 18.45 |
| 2 | 0.01 | 2 | 1.00 | 2 | 0.68 | 2 | 13.45 |
| 3 | 0.30 | 3 | 5.95 | 3 | 5.55 | 3 | 48.95 |
| 4 | 0.17 | 4 | 0.14 | 4 | 1.95 | 4 | 19.45 |
| 5 | 0.06 | 5 | 0.77 | 5 | 2.45 | 5 | 25.95 |

**Activity 3: Researching**

Check students' work.

## ✔ Checkpoint Quiz 1

**1.** $2 \times 2; 4$  **2.** $1 \times 3; 6$  **3.** $3 \times 3; 0$

**4.** $\begin{bmatrix} 12 & -1 \\ 10 & 5 \\ -5 & 4 \end{bmatrix}$  **5.** $\begin{bmatrix} -20 & 10 \\ -15 & -5 \end{bmatrix}$  **6.** $\begin{bmatrix} 15 & -3 \\ 21 & 18 \\ -6 & 0 \end{bmatrix}$

**7.** $\begin{bmatrix} 24 & -2 \\ 20 & 10 \\ -10 & 8 \end{bmatrix}$  **8.** $\begin{bmatrix} -16 & 12 \\ 3 & 14 \end{bmatrix}$  **9.** $\begin{bmatrix} -2 & -1 \\ 4 & 7 \\ 1 & -4 \end{bmatrix}$  **10.** C

## ✔ Checkpoint Quiz 2

**1.** $A'\,(5, -5); B'\,(6, -1); C'\,(1, -4)$
**2.** $A'\,(4, -12); B'\,(8, 4); C'\,(-12, -8)$
**3.** $A'\,(1, 3); B'\,(2, -1); C'\,(-3, 2)$
**4.** $A'\,(-3, -1); B'\,(1, -2); C'\,(-2, 3)$

**5.** $\begin{bmatrix} -\frac{7}{4} & -\frac{1}{4} \\ \frac{5}{2} & \frac{1}{2} \end{bmatrix}$  **6.** $\begin{bmatrix} \frac{1}{6} & -\frac{1}{3} \\ \frac{5}{6} & -\frac{2}{3} \end{bmatrix}$  **7.** no inverse  **8.** $\begin{bmatrix} -2 \\ 3 \end{bmatrix}$

**9.** $\begin{bmatrix} 5 & 4 \\ 0 & 1 \end{bmatrix}$  **10.** $\begin{bmatrix} 4 \\ \frac{1}{2} \\ -\frac{1}{2} \end{bmatrix}$

## Chapter Test, Form A

**1a.** $\begin{bmatrix} 85 & -34 \\ 104 & -27 \\ 107 & 7 \\ 98 & 30 \\ 103 & -18 \\ 111 & 29 \end{bmatrix}$; $6 \times 2$  **1b.** 30  **2.** $\begin{bmatrix} 2 & 7 \\ 2 & -4 \end{bmatrix}$

**3.** $\begin{bmatrix} 23 & 20 & -2 \\ 29 & 12 & 30 \\ 21 & 24 & 3 \end{bmatrix}$  **4.** $\begin{bmatrix} 5 & 14 \\ 6 & 12 \\ 18 & 52 \end{bmatrix}$  **5.** $\begin{bmatrix} -9 & -30 \\ -63 & 12 \end{bmatrix}$

**6.** product undefined  **7.** $\begin{bmatrix} 8 & 3 \\ 0 & 0 \end{bmatrix}$

**8a.** $\left(\frac{1}{2}, \frac{1}{2}\right), \left(\frac{3}{2}, 2\right), \left(0, -\frac{5}{2}\right)$  **8b.** $(4, 3), (6, 6), (3, -3)$
**8c.** $(-1, -1), (-3, -4), (0, 5)$  **8d.** $(1, 1), (4, 3), (-5, 0)$
**9.** $-13$  **10.** $-1$  **11.** 52

**12.** $\begin{bmatrix} \frac{1}{3} & -\frac{1}{3} \\ -\frac{1}{2} & 1 \end{bmatrix}$  **13.** no inverse

**14.** $\begin{bmatrix} -1 & -1 & 4 \\ 1 & 2 & -5 \\ 0 & -1 & 2 \end{bmatrix}$  **15.** no inverse  **16.** $\begin{bmatrix} -11 \\ 9 \end{bmatrix}$

**17.** $\begin{bmatrix} -2 & 1 \\ -2 & 1 \end{bmatrix}$  **18.** $\begin{bmatrix} 7 & -2 & -6 \\ 15 & 1 & -2 \end{bmatrix}$  **19.** $\begin{bmatrix} -20 & 1 \\ 26 & -1 \end{bmatrix}$

**20.** $\begin{bmatrix} \frac{1}{4} & \frac{1}{2} \\ \frac{1}{2} & 1 \end{bmatrix}$  **21.** $\begin{bmatrix} -\frac{3}{4} & \frac{1}{4} \\ 1 & -1 \end{bmatrix}$  **22.** $(0, -2)$

**23.** $(-2, -3, 4)$  **24.** $(-2, -2)$  **25.** $(0, 1, 3)$  **26.** Answers may vary. Check students' work  **27.** Yes; Check students' work  **28.** $2 \times 4$  **29.** $.75, \$1.00

# Chapter 4 Answers (continued)

## Chapter Test, Form B

**1a.** $\begin{bmatrix} -80 & 100 \\ -45 & 134 \\ -2 & 109 \\ -51 & 112 \\ -50 & 116 \\ -58 & 120 \end{bmatrix}$; $6 \times 2$  **1b.** $-45$  **2.** $\begin{bmatrix} 2 & -5 \\ -3 & 30 \end{bmatrix}$

**3.** $\begin{bmatrix} 16 & 7 & 26 \\ 20 & 18 & -17 \\ 18 & 15 & -1 \end{bmatrix}$  **4.** $\begin{bmatrix} 3 & 3 \\ 14 & 26 \\ 16 & 31 \end{bmatrix}$  **5.** $\begin{bmatrix} 40 & -80 \\ -10 & -5 \end{bmatrix}$

**6.** product undefined  **7.** $\begin{bmatrix} 2 & 3 \\ 4 & 0 \end{bmatrix}$

**8a.** $\left(\frac{3}{4}, \frac{1}{4}\right), \left(\frac{3}{4}, -2\right), \left(-1, \frac{1}{4}\right), (-1, -2)$

**8b.** $(-1, -1), (-1, -10), (-8, -1), (-8, -10)$
**8c.** $(-1, 3), (8, 3), (-1, -4), (8, -4)$
**8d.** $(-1, -3), (8, -3), (-1, 4), (8, 4)$  **9.** $-2$  **10.** $-82$
**11.** 56

**12.** $\begin{bmatrix} \frac{3}{2} & -\frac{5}{8} \\ -1 & \frac{1}{2} \end{bmatrix}$  **13.** no inverse

**14.** $\begin{bmatrix} -\frac{1}{6} & \frac{1}{6} & \frac{1}{3} \\ \frac{2}{3} & \frac{1}{3} & -\frac{7}{3} \\ -\frac{1}{3} & -\frac{2}{3} & \frac{8}{3} \end{bmatrix}$  **15.** no inverse

**16.** $\begin{bmatrix} -23 \\ 31 \end{bmatrix}$  **17.** $\begin{bmatrix} -1 & -5 \\ 16 & 9 \end{bmatrix}$  **18.** $\begin{bmatrix} -6 & 15 & 8 \\ 2 & -1 & 3 \end{bmatrix}$

**19.** $\begin{bmatrix} -6 & 1 \\ 6 & 0 \end{bmatrix}$  **20.** $\begin{bmatrix} 2 & -2 \\ 4 & -11 \end{bmatrix}$  **21.** $\begin{bmatrix} 9 & 2 \\ -7 & -3 \end{bmatrix}$  **22.** $(1, 2)$
**23.** $(0, -2, 2)$  **24.** $(-3, 2)$  **25.** $(-4, 2, 1)$

**26.** $\begin{bmatrix} -8 & 10 \\ 10 & -14 \end{bmatrix}$; $\begin{bmatrix} 1 & -7 \\ 5 & -23 \end{bmatrix}$; no  **27.** the identity matrix with

the same dimensions  **28.** $20 \times 50$  **29.** $2050 at 7.5\%, \$3950$
at 8\%

## Alternative Assessment, Form C
### TASK 1 Scoring Guide:

**3**  Matrix is constructed correctly. Student discussion is detailed enough to indicate a clear understanding of the properties of matrices. Addition, subtraction, and multiplication operations are performed with no mistakes. Inverse matrix is correct or, if none exists, explanation is provided.

**2**  Matrix is constructed correctly. Student discussion is detailed. Addition, subtraction, and multiplication of matrices are mostly correct but contain minor errors. Inverse matrix contains minor errors or explanation is not sufficiently detailed if no inverse exists.

**1**  Matrix contains minor errors. Operations are attempted but include major errors. Inverse is not included, or explanation as to why no inverse exists is not included.

**0**  Student makes no attempt, or no response is given.

### TASK 2 Scoring Guide:

**a.** $\begin{array}{cccc} a & b & c & d \end{array}$ $\begin{bmatrix} 1 & 2 & 2 & 1 \\ 4 & 4 & 3 & 3 \end{bmatrix}$  **b.** $\begin{bmatrix} -2 & -2 & -2 & -2 \\ -1 & -1 & -1 & -1 \end{bmatrix}$

**c.**  matrix addition

**d.**  $a'(-1, 3), b'(0, 3), c'(0, 2), d'(-1, 2)$

**e.**  $a'(2, 8), b'(4, 8), c'(4, 6), d'(2, 6)$

**3**  Student organizes vertices correctly into matrix. Matrix of the translation is written correctly. Correct answers are provided to all questions.

**2**  Student organizes vertices correctly into matrix. Matrix of the translation is written correctly and correct answers are provided to three of the last four questions.

**1**  Student organizes vertices correctly into matrix. Translation matrix contains significant errors. Two or three of the last three questions are answered incorrectly.

**0**  Student makes no attempt, or no response is given.

### TASK 3 Scoring Guide:

**a.** $\begin{bmatrix} 1 & -a \\ -\frac{1}{a^2} & \frac{2}{a} \end{bmatrix}$  **b.** $A^{-1}A = AA^{-1} = \begin{bmatrix} 1 & 0 \\ 0 & 1 \end{bmatrix}$

**c.**  No; matrix multiplication is not commutative.

**3**  Inverse matrix is correct. Multiplication of $AA^{-1}$ and $A^{-1}A$ gives $I$. Student indicates that multiplication of matrices is not commutative. Student discussion is detailed and clear enough to indicate a clear understanding of the properties of matrices.

**2**  Inverse matrix and multiplication are mostly correct but contain minor errors. Student discussion is detailed.

**1**  Inverse matrix and multiplication include errors. Two or three questions are answered incorrectly.

**0**  Student makes no attempt, or no response is given.

**TASK 4 Scoring Guide:**

   **a.** $(1.25, -2)$  **b.** $(-3, 1.5)$  **c.** $(-9, 13, 6)$  **d.** $(13, 8, 12)$

**3**  Student solves all systems correctly using inverse matrices. Student shows the process for calculating the inverse and multiplying to solve $X = A^{-1}B$.

**2**  Student solves two systems correctly and makes minor errors in the solutions to the other systems. Student shows the process and all calculations.

**1**  Student solves one system correctly, while the others contain major errors.

**0**  Student makes no attempt, or no response is given.

## Cumulative Review

**1.** C  **2.** C  **3.** A  **4.** A  **5.** C  **6.** B  **7.** D  **8.** B  **9.** D  **10.** D
**11.** C  **12.** D  **13.** C  **14.** D  **15.** C  **16.** B  **17.** Answers may vary. Sample: preimage: $(8, 4), (16, 8), (0, 0)$; image: $(4, 2)$, $(8, 4), (0, 0)$  **18.** Check students' work.